THE FIRESIDE BOOK OF
CHILDREN'S SONGS

COLLECTED & EDITED BY MARIE WINN
MUSICAL ARRANGEMENTS BY ALLAN MILLER
ILLUSTRATIONS BY JOHN ALCORN

SIMON AND SCHUSTER, NEW YORK

The authors wish to thank the following for permission to include copyrighted material:

J. B. Cramer & Co., Ltd., London, for "All Through the Night" by Sir Harold Boulton; E. P. Dutton & Company, Inc. for "Cottleston Pie" from the book Winnie-the-Pooh by A. A. Milne. Copyright 1926 by E. P. Dutton & Co., Inc. Renewal, 1954, by A. A. Milne. Reprinted and set to music by permission of the publishers; Folkways Records & Service Corp. for "Mi Burro" from Children's Songs from Spain, sung by Karen James and Isabelita Alonso on Folkways Record #FC 7746; "La Poulette Grise" from French Folk Songs for Children, sung by Alan Mills on Folkways Record #FC 7208; "Kitty Alone" from Children's Songs and Games from the Southern Mountains, sung by Jean Ritchie on Folkways Record #FC 754; "There Was a Man and He Was Mad" from American Folk Songs for Children, sung by Pete Seeger on Folkways Record #FC 701; and "If All the Raindrops Were Lemondrops and Gumdrops," from Camp Songs, sung by Pete Seeger on Folkways Record #FC 7028; General Music Publishing Company for "Little White Duck," copyright 1950 by General Music Publishing Co., Inc.; Harcourt, Brace & World, Inc. for "The Animal Fair," "Horse Named Bill" and "By'm Bye" from The American Songbag by Carl Sandburg; Houghton Mifflin Company for Richard Chase's Hullabaloo and Other Singing Folk Dances, published by Houghton Mifflin Company. Used by permission; Hal David and Norman Monath for "The Choo-Choo Train." Copyright 1951 by Jac Music Company; Novello & Co., Ltd., London, for "Rose, Rose, and Up She Rises" from English Folk Songs of the Southern Appalachians, collected by Cecil Sharp and edited by Maud Karpeles, copyright 1932 by Novello & Co., Ltd.; Peer International Corporation for "I Know an Old Lady," copyright 1952 by Peer International (Canada), Ltd. Copyright © 1960 by Peer International (Canada), Ltd. Used by permission; Janet E. Tobitt for "Kookaburra" by Marion Sinclair from The Ditty Bag by Janet E. Tobitt, copyright 1946; Charles Seeger for "Clap Your Hands" from American Folk Songs for Children, copyright 1948 by Ruth Crawford Seeger, published by Doubleday and Company, Inc.; and "My Old Hen" and "The Animal Song," from Animal Folk Songs for Children, copyright 1950 by Ruth Crawford Seeger, published by Doubleday and Company, Inc.; Sterling Publishing Company for "Pass the Shoe," adapted from Best Singing Games for Children of All Ages by Edgar Bley © 1957 by Sterling Publishing Co., N.Y.
Sterling Publishing Co., N.Y.; Silver Burdett & Co. for "Good Morning to You" by Abbie Farwell Brown, from The Progressive Music Series, Book 1; copyright 1914 by Silver Burdett & Co., renewed 1942.

LIBRARY OF CONGRESS CATALOG CARD NUMBER: 65-17108
MANUFACTURED IN THE UNITED STATES OF AMERICA
BY AMERICAN BOOK-STRATFORD PRESS, INC., NEW YORK
MUSIC AUTOGRAPHING BY MAXWELL WEANER

CONTENTS

SECTION THREE
NURSERY SONGS

SECTION FOUR
SILLY SONGS

SECTION FIVE
SINGING GAMES AND ROUNDS

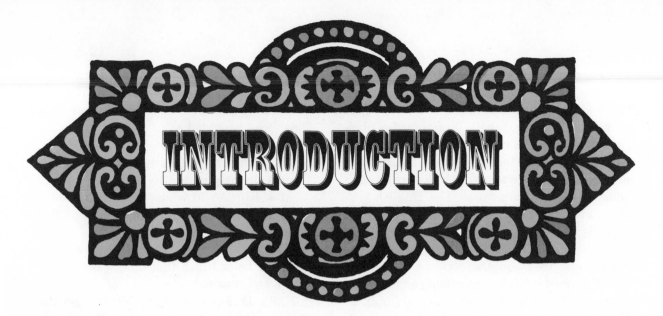

INTRODUCTION

THE SONGS that make up the *Fireside Book of Children's Songs* are children's songs not necessarily because they were written for children or meant to be sung only by children, but because, whatever their origin, they appeal to children. Children like to listen to them and to sing them again and again and again.

Bedtime is a traditional time for singing to children and with children, for singing is a beautiful way to end a day and a calm, quiet way to begin the night. Any song may be sung at bedtime—indeed, some families like to sing rounds—and children often request long, cumulative songs to postpone the final good nights. But there is a certain category of songs meant especially for nighttime, usually lullabies, and most of the best known of these, as well as some new and beautiful ones, are found in the first section, "Good Morning and Good Night." And, as the title of this section indicates, there are also some songs for getting up in the morning.

Children feel a special closeness to animals and that is why there is a special section that bears the title "Birds and Beasts." The variety of songs about animals that children particularly enjoy is remarkable. There are songs that feature the noises animals make, like "I Bought Me a Rooster" and "Three Little Piggies"; there are animal songs that tell a story, like "Little White Duck" or "Mister Frog Went A-Courting"; there are some sad ones, like "Old Blue"—and a few that are downright silly.

In the third section, called "Nursery Songs," are found many of the most beloved traditional songs for children—songs that parents sang when *they* were children. These are songs for the very youngest children, the first songs most children learn. Here is "Jack and Jill," and "Twinkle, Twinkle, Little Star," and some old, old ones that grandparents and great-grandparents might be likely to remember, like "Bobby Shafto" and "The Little Nut Tree." And here, too, are a few new ones that may well become the traditional songs of generations to come.

There is no question but that at times all children love to be silly. The "Silly Songs" of Section Four appeal to children mostly for their delicious lack of sense. These are songs children like especially to sing in groups—songs that never seem to lose their freshness and never fail to inspire a few giggles. Songs that turn the world topsy-turvy, like "Fooba-Wooba John" or "Boom, Boom, Ain't It Great to Be Crazy," songs that tell outlandish stories, like "A Capital Ship," and songs that are sheer nonsense, like "Lloyd George Knew My Father" or "My Uncle Roasted a Kangaroo"—these have an immense appeal to all children, and may even provoke a grin from grownups.

There is, of course, an inevitable amount of overlapping, for many animal songs and nursery songs are as silly as they come, and some of those in the Silly Song section happen to be about animals.

Many children's songs are built around

games, and so there is a final section which includes singing games of different kinds—circle games, imitative, follow-the-leader-type games, and rounds. Simple directions for playing the games are provided.

This collection includes many songs from other parts of the world which were originally sung in foreign languages. The English versions of many of these songs cannot strictly be called translations, but rather rewritings on the same theme. In this way an attempt has been made to avoid the strange, unnatural sound of most literal translations, and to make some of the concepts sound more familiar. Thus a grey hen is transformed into a big brown dog and lilac slippers become lollipops. However, for those who might enjoy singing these songs in their original languages, these have been provided; with languages less familiar and more difficult to pronounce, there are phonetic transliterations instead.

The piano accompaniments are intended to capture the individual spirit of each song, and yet they are easy enough for amateur pianists to read at sight. In addition, guitar chords have been provided.

The compiler wishes to acknowledge with thanks the help of the following:

Alan Rinzler, in whose mind this book was born and whose fine taste was a guide in the selection of these songs.

Henry W. Simon, editor, adviser and friend, who has helped in a thousand ways, both literary and musical.

Emile D. Poklitar of the Music Operations Department of the Columbia Broadcasting System, for aid in locating sources.

Mrs. Mary Ann Porcher, for advice and suggestions out of her experience with children and children's music.

The New York Public Library—especial thanks for help in every phase of the making of this book.

GOOD MORNING TO YOU

A popular camp and school morning song.

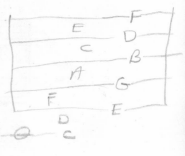

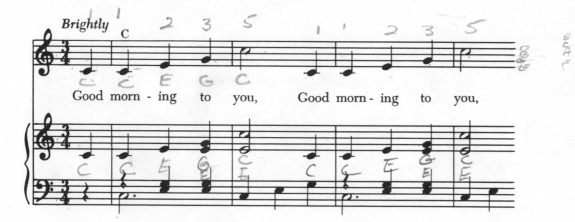

Good morn - ing to you, Good morn - ing to you,

We're all in our plac - es, With sun - shine - y fac - es,

Is this not the way To start a new day!

HUSH, LITTLE BABY

*Children delight in the catalog of presents promised
in this Southern lullaby.*

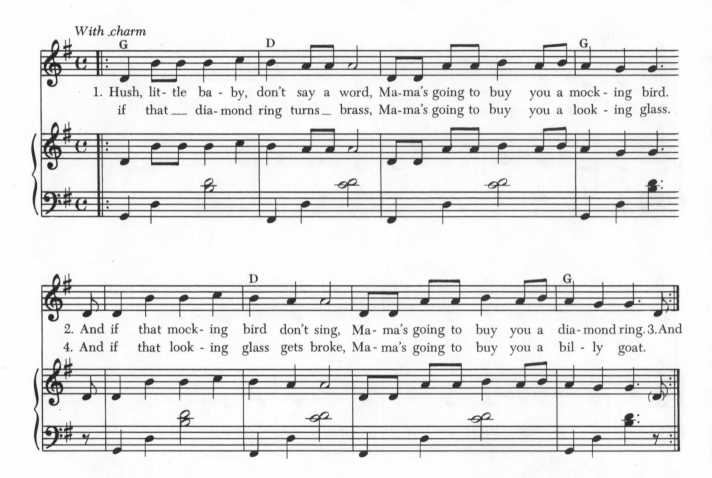

With charm

1. Hush, lit- tle ba - by, don't say a word, Ma-ma's going to buy you a mock - ing bird.
   if that ___ dia- mond ring turns ___ brass, Ma-ma's going to buy you a look - ing glass.

2. And if that mock - ing bird don't sing, Ma-ma's going to buy you a dia- mond ring. 3. And
4. And if that look - ing glass gets broke, Ma-ma's going to buy you a bil - ly goat.

5. And if that billy goat won't pull,
   Mama's going to buy you a cart and bull.

6. And if that cart and bull turn over,
   Mama's going to buy you a dog named Rover.

7. And if that dog named Rover won't bark,
   Mama's going to buy you a horse and cart.

8. And if that horse and cart fall down,
   You'll still be the sweetest little baby in town.

12

BY'M BYE

The stars beginning to come out at night inspired the idea for this lullaby,
a part of an old Negro spiritual.

By'm bye, by'm bye; Stars shin-ing:
1. Num-ber, num-ber one, num-ber
2. Num-ber, num-ber four, num-ber

two, num-ber three, good Lord, By'm bye, by'm bye, good Lord, By'm bye.
five, num-ber six,

ROSE, ROSE, AND UP SHE RISES

A good, rousing morning song that sounds much like the chorus of the familiar sea shanty "The Drunken Sailor." But this version was found in Kentucky, many a mile from the sea.

1. Rose, rose, and up she ris-es, Rose, rose, and up she ris-es,
2. What shall we do with sleep-y Bil-ly,* What shall we do with sleep-y Bil-ly,*

Rose, rose, and up she ris-es, Earl-eye in the morn-ing.
What shall we do with sleep-y Bil-ly,* Earl-eye in the morn-ing.

* Or any other name — girl or boy.

3. Wake {her / him} up and shake {her / him} up,
   Wake her up and shake her up,
   Wake her up and shake her up,
   Earleye in the morning.

4. Hooray and up she rises,
   Hooray and up she rises,
   Hooray and up she rises,
   Earleye in the morning.

14

Sleep, Baby, Sleep

[SCHLAF, KINDLEIN, SCHLAF]

A beloved German lullaby that has become known the world over.

Softly, moving

1. Sleep, ba-by, sleep, Thy fa-ther guards the sheep, Thy mo-ther shakes the
2. *Schlaf, Kind-lein, schlaf, Der Va-ter hüt' die Schaf, Die Mut-ter schüt-telt's*

dream-land tree, And from it fall sweet dreams for thee, Sleep, ba-by, sleep.
Bäum-e-lein, Da fällt her-ab ein Träum-e-lein, Schlaf, Kind-lein, schlaf.

16

LAZY MARY

A well-known getting-up song that cannot be simpler in the mother's request,
or more typical in the child's answer. Other children's names
are often substituted for "Mary."

With bounce

1. La - zy Ma - ry, will you get up, Will you get up, will you get up?
2. No, no, mo - ther, I won't get up, I won't get up, I won't get up,

La - zy Ma - ry, will you get up, Will you get up to - day?____
No, no, mo - ther, I won't get up, I won't get up to - day. ____

Brahms' Lullaby

Perhaps the most famous lullaby ever composed. The words were written by Brahms' publisher and close friend Fritz Simrock.

ADAPTED BY A.M.

Tenderly

1. Lul- la- by and good night, With roses be- dight,
2. *Gu- ten A - bend, gut' Nacht, Mit Ro- sen be- dacht,*

With lil- ies be- spread Is ba- by's wee bed.
Mit Näg- lein be- steckt, Schlüpf un - ter die Deck.

18

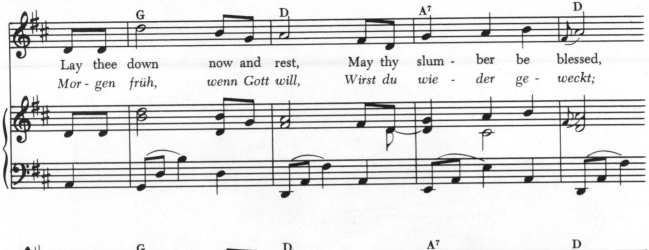

Lay thee down now and rest, May thy slum - ber be blessed,
Mor - gen früh, wenn Gott will, Wirst du wie - der ge - weckt;

Lay thee down now and rest, May thy slum - ber be blessed.
Mor - gen früh, wenn Gott will, Wirst du wie - der ge - weckt.

ROCK-A-BYE BABY

The most widely known and loved lullaby of all.

Rock - a-bye ba - by on the tree - top,

When the wind blows the cra - dle will rock,

When the bough breaks the cra - dle will fall,

And down will come ba - by, cra - dle and all.

ALL THE PRETTY LITTLE HORSES

One of the most haunting lullabies to come out of the Old South.

1. Hush-a-bye, don't you cry, Go to sleep-y lit-tle ba - by;
2. Mam-my loves, and pap-py loves, And mam-my loves her lit-tle ba - by;

When you wake, you shall have cake And all the pret-ty lit-tle hor - ses.
Go to sleep, go __ to sleep, Go to sleep, you lit-tle ba - by.

Black and bay, dap-ple and gray, Coach and six __ white __ hor - ses.

Vocal line collected, adapted and arranged by John A. Lomax and Alan Lomax.
Copyright © 1934 and renewed 1962 by Ludlow Music, Inc.,
New York, N.Y. Used by permission.

Wake Up, Jacob!

A cowboy getting-up holler frequently heard in Western camps of the past.
Any child's name may be substituted for Jacob—and the last line
must be hollered at the top of the lungs.

As freely as possible; the rhythm should follow the words

Wake up, Ja - cob, day's a - break - in', Peas in the pot and ___ hoe - cakes bak - in'. Ba - con's in the pan and cof - fee's in the pot, ___ Come on round and get it while it's hot. ___ Wake snakes and bite a biscuit!

COTTON-EYED JOE

Cotton-eyed Joe came from Tennessee, but who he was, if anyone, is not known.
Perhaps "cotton-eyed" is just a lovely way of saying "sleepy."

Where did you come from, Where did you go? Where did you come from, Cot-ton-eyed Joe?

Come for to see you, Come for to sing, Come for to show you My gold-and-dia-mond ring.

Vocal line collected, adapted and arranged by John A. Lomax and Alan Lomax.
Copyright © 1934 and renewed 1962 by Ludlow Music, Inc.,
New York, N.Y. Used by permission.

ALL THROUGH THE NIGHT

A beloved Welsh lullaby with words by Sir Harold Boulton.

Smoothly (notes with stems up may be sung with "ooh" as descant)

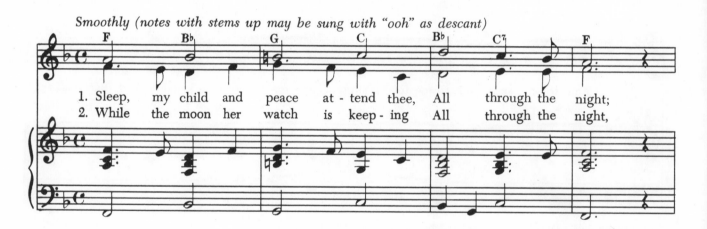

1. Sleep, my child and peace at-tend thee, All through the night;
2. While the moon her watch is keep-ing All through the night,

Guard - ian an - gels God will send thee, All through the night;
While the wea - ry world is sleep - ing All through the night.

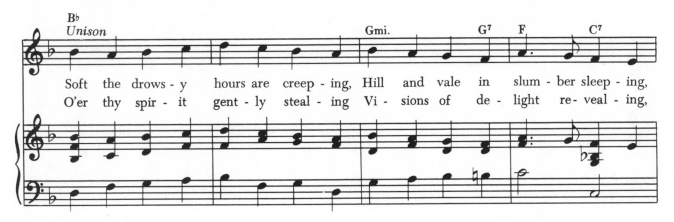

Soft the drows-y hours are creep-ing, Hill and vale in slum-ber sleep-ing,
O'er thy spir-it gent-ly steal-ing Vi-sions of de-light re-veal-ing,

I my lov-ing vi-gil keep-ing, All through the night.
Breathes a pure and ho-ly feel-ing All through the night.

KITTY ALONE

A Southern version of a song that goes back to the eighteenth,
possibly even the sixteenth century in England.

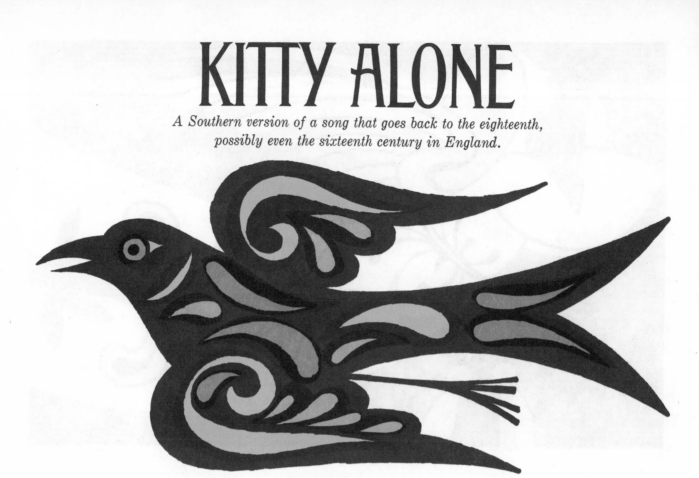

Softly flowing

1. Saw a crow a-fly-ing low, Kit-ty a-lone, kit-ty a-lone;
2. In ____ came a lit-tle bat, Kit-ty a-lone, kit-ty a-lone;

Saw a crow a-fly-ing low, Kit-ty a-lone, a-lye;
In ____ came a lit-tle bat, Kit-ty a-lone, a-lye;

C ... **F**

Saw a crow a-fly-ing low And a cat a-spin-ning tow,
In ___ came a lit-tle bat With some but-ter and some fat,

C ... **C** **G** **C**

Kit-ty a-lone, a-lye; Rock-um-a-rye-ree.
Kit-ty a-lone, a-lye; Rock-um-a-rye-ree.

3. Next came in was a honeybee, kitty alone, kitty alone;
Next came in was a honeybee, kitty alone, a-lye;
Next came in was a honeybee with a fiddle across his knee,
Kitty alone, a-lye; rock-um-a-rye-ree.

4. Next came in was little Pete, kitty alone, kitty alone;
Next came in was little Pete, kitty alone, a-lye;
Next came in was little Pete fixing around to go to sleep,
Kitty alone, a-lye; rock-um-a-rye-ree.

5. Bee-o, bye-o, baby-o, kitty alone, kitty alone;
Bee-o, bye-o, baby-o, kitty alone, a-lye;
Bee-o, bye-o, baby-o, bye-o, bee-o, baby-o,
Kitty alone, a-lye; rock-um-a-rye-ree.

29

THE OLD GREY HEN

[LA POULETTE GRISE]

In this old French cradle song each verse tells of a different colored hen.
In the English version the hen becomes a dog and a fish, but the
idea remains the same, and children enjoy hearing
their own names sung in the song.

1. We've got an old grey hen ____ In our chick-en pen, ____
1. *C'est la pou-let-te gri - se, Qui pond dans l'é-gli - se,*

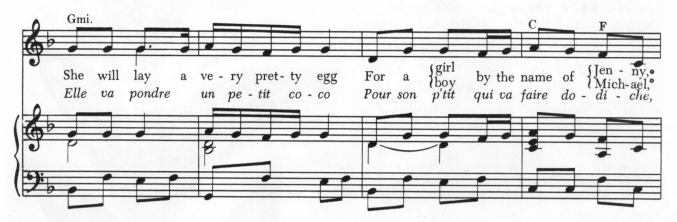

She will lay a ve-ry pret-ty egg For a {girl {boy} by the name of {Jen - ny,✻ {Mich-ael,✻
Elle va pondre un pe-tit co-co Pour son p'tit qui va faire do-di - che,

30

She will lay a ve-ry pret-ty egg For a {girl / boy} if she goes to sleep.

Elle va pond-re un pe-tit co-co Pour son p'tit qui va faire do-do.

Sleep, {Jen-ny,* / Mich-ael,*} sleep. _____

Do - diche, do - do. _____

*Any other name may be substituted.

2. We've got a big brown dog,
   Sleeping on a log,
   He will bring a pretty little ball
   For a boy whose name is Bobby,
   He will bring a pretty little ball
   For a boy if he goes to sleep.
   Sleep, Bobby, sleep.

3. We've got a little fish,
   Swimming in a dish,
   She will tell a funny fishy tale
   To a girl whose name is Nancy,
   She will tell a funny fishy tale
   To a girl if she goes to sleep.
   Sleep, Nancy, sleep.

2. C'est la poulette blanche,
   Qui pond dans les branches,
   Elle va pondre un petit coco
   Pour son p'tit qui va faire dodiche,
   Elle va pondre un petit coco
   Pour son p'tit qui va faire dodo.
   Dodiche, dodo.

3. C'est la poulette brune,
   Qui pond dans la lune,
   Elle va pondre un petit coco
   Pour son p'tit qui va faire dodiche,
   Elle va pondre un petit coco
   Pour son p'tit qui va faire dodo.
   Dodiche, dodo.

BABY SITTER'S LULLABY

[VIGNDIG A FREMD KIND]

When Mother works, who will sing the baby to sleep?
The baby sitter, of course, says this Yiddish lullaby.

1. Young girls they dance and they flirt and flit, While I ___ stay in - doors here and
2. Zolst a - zoy le - bn un zayn ge - zint, Vi ich ___ vel dir zi - tsn un

ba - by sit, Ay - loo - loo, hush - a - bye. Your
vi - gn's kind, Ay - lyu - lyu, sha - sha - sha. Dayn

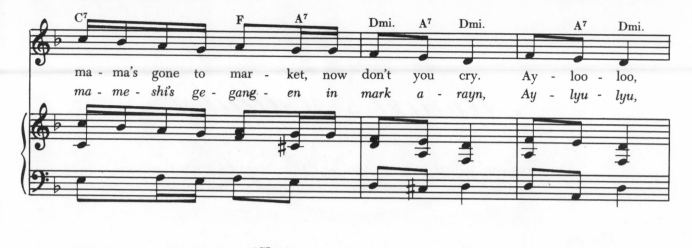

ma - ma's gone to mar - ket, now don't you cry. Ay - loo - loo,
ma - me - shi's ge - gang - en in mark a - rayn, Ay - lyu - lyu,

hush - a - bye. Your ma - ma's com - ing back soon, so don't you cry.
shlof, mayn kind. Dayn ma - me - shi vet ki - men gich un ge - shvind.

Mozart's Lullaby

*The piano part, only slightly modified here from Mozart's original version,
is as important and expressive in this lullaby as the vocal line.*

Flowing

1. Sleep, ba - by, sleep, and good night,　　All the birds are a - sleep out of sight,
Schla - fe, mein Prinz - chen, schlaf ein,　　Es ruhn nun Schäf - chen und Vög - e - lein,

Qui - et the lambs on the hill,　　E - ven the bum - ble bee's still,
Gar - ten und Wie - se ver - stummt,　　Auch nicht ein Bien - chen mehr summt,

On - ly the man in the moon　　Still is a - nod - ding, but soon
Lu - na mit sil - ber - nem Schein　　Guck - et zum Fen - ster her - ein,

O - ver him slum-ber will creep,   Sleep, ba - by, sleep, go to sleep.   Good
Schla - fe beim sil - ber - nen Schein,   *Schla- fe, mein Prinz-chen, schlaf ein.*   *Schlaf*

night, _____ Good night.
ein, _____ *schlaf ein.*

Raindrops

[HEJ PADA PADA]

An old Slovak lullaby with a mixture of major and minor
typical of Slovak songs.

Gently
Emi.
G

1. Rain-drops a - fall - ing from the skies, Ti- red and sleep- y, close your eyes.
2. *Hej pa- da pa- da ro- sič- ka, Spa- ly by mo- je o - čič- ka.*

Ti - red   and sleep - y   While the skies are weep - ing,
Spa - ly   by mo   je,   Spa - ly by aj tvo - je,

Weep - ing   and sing - ing you their lul - la - bies.
Spa - ly   by du - ša mo - ja o - bo - je.

Ti - red   and sleep - y   While the skies are weep - ing,
Spa - ly   by mo - je,   Spa - ly by aj tvo - je,

Weep - ing   and sing - ing you their lul - la - bies.
Spa - ly   by du - ša mo - ja o - bo - je.

THE EVENING IS COMING

Easily

1. The eve-ning is com-ing, the sun sinks to rest,
2. Here comes the po-ny, his work is all done,

The birds are all fly-ing straight home to their nests,
Down through the mea-dow he takes a good run,

"Caw, caw," says the crow as he flies o-ver-head,
Up go his heels ___ and down goes his head,

It's time lit-tle chil-dren were go-ing to bed.
It's time lit-tle chil-dren were go-ing to bed.

40

THE ANIMAL SONG

A mad catalog of birds and beasts to the tune of "Little Brown Jug."

Lyrics (verse 1 and 2, under music):

1. Al - li - ga - tor, hedge - hog, ant - eat - er, bear, Rat - tle - snake, buf - fa - lo, an - a - con - da, hare.
2. Bull - frog, ___ wood - chuck, wol - ver - ine, ___ goose, Whip - poor - will, chip - munk, jack - al, ___ moose.

3. Mud turtle, whale, glowworm, bat,
   Salamander, snail and Maltese cat.

4. Polecat, dog, wild otter, rat,
   Pelican, hog, dodo and bat.

5. House rat, toe rat, white bear, doe,
   Chickadee, peacock, bobolink and crow.

MY OLD HEN

A Wisconsin parody of the old English nursery rhyme:

Hickety, pickety, my black hen,
She lays eggs for the gentlemen,
Sometimes nine and sometimes ten,
Hickety, pickety, my black hen.

Fast, with energy

Dmi.   Gmi.   Dmi.

My old hen's a good old hen, She lays eggs for the rail-road men.

Gmi.   Dmi.

Some-times one, some-times two, Some-times e-nough for the whole blamed crew.

Cluck, old hen, cluck, I tell you, Cluck, old hen, or I'm gon-na sell you.

Cluck, old hen, cluck, I say, Cluck, old hen, or I'll give you a-way. _____

OLD MOLLY HARE

Animals that are hunted for food are often the subjects of folk songs. But in this song of Negro origin the hunted becomes the hunter, the sort of topsy-turvy humor children have always loved.

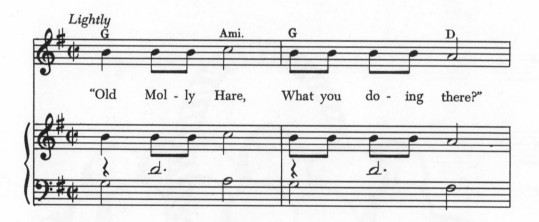

Lightly

"Old Mol - ly Hare, What you do - ing there?"

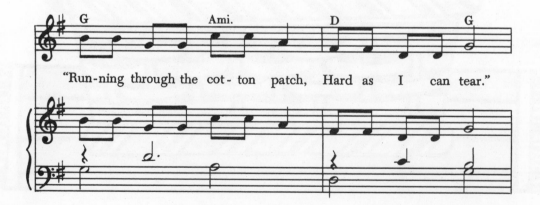

"Run-ning through the cot - ton patch, Hard as I can tear."

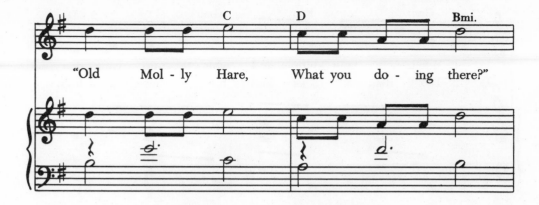

"Old Mol-ly Hare, What you do-ing there?"

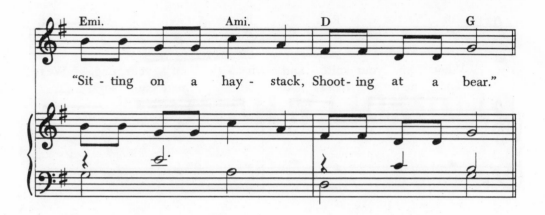

"Sit-ting on a hay-stack, Shoot-ing at a bear."

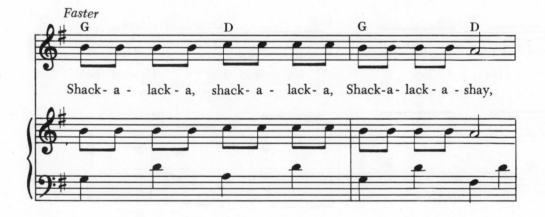

Shack-a-lack-a, shack-a-lack-a, Shack-a-lack-a-shay,

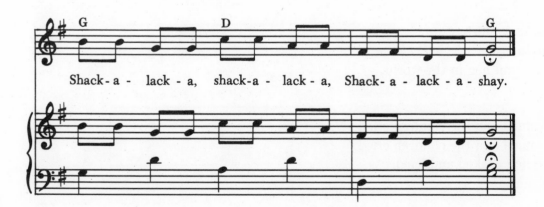

Shack-a-lack-a, shack-a-lack-a, Shack-a-lack-a-shay.

GROUND HOG

A ground hog is more commonly known as a woodchuck. The words "Ground Hog!" in this Appalachian ballad are usually half sung, half hollered.

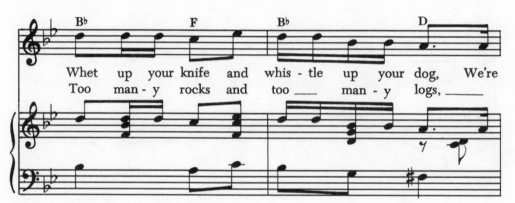

1. Whet up your knife and whis-tle up your dog,
2. Too man-y rocks and too ___ man-y logs,

Whet up your knife and whis-tle up your dog, We're
Too man-y rocks and too ___ man-y logs, ___

go-ing to the hol-low to catch a ground hog. Ground hog!
Too ___ man-y rocks ___ to catch ___ ground hogs. Ground hog!

3. Here he comes all in a whirl,
   Here he comes all in a whirl,
   He's the biggest ground hog in the world.
   Ground hog!

4. The children screamed and the children cried,
   The children screamed and the children cried,
   They love ground hog cooked and fried.
   Ground hog!

46

I BOUGHT ME A ROOSTER

*Cumulative songs about animals and their particular noises are found in almost
every language. This one is well known in the southern mountains,
but is sung in slightly different versions throughout the United States.*

1. I bought me a roost-er and the roost-er pleased me,
I fed my roost-er on the bay-ber-ry tree,
My lit-tle roost-er goes cock - a-dood-le doo, dee

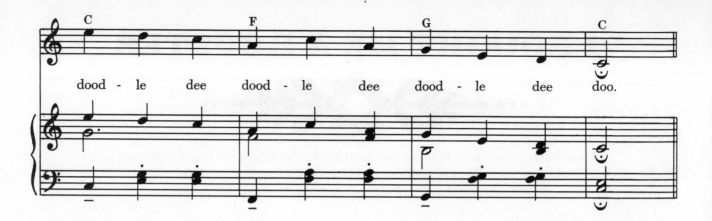

doo - dle dee dood - le dee dood - le dee doo.

(For verses 2-6 begin here)

2. I bought me a cat and the cat pleased me,
3. I bought me a dog and the dog pleased me,

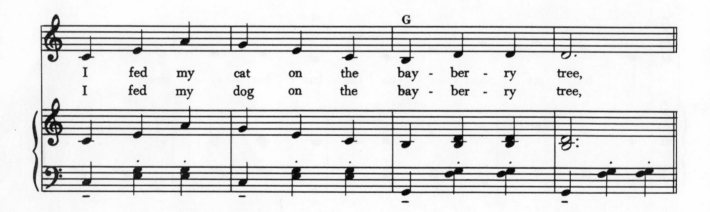

I fed my cat on the bay - ber - ry tree,
I fed my dog on the bay - ber - ry tree,

2. My lit - tle cat goes meow, meow, meow,
3. { My lit - tle dog goes arf, arf, arf,
    My lit - tle cat goes meow, meow, meow,

48

My lit - tle roost - er goes cock - a - dood - le doo, dee
dood - le dee dood - le dee dood - le dee doo.

4. I bought me a pig and the pig pleased me,
   I fed my pig on the bayberry tree,
   My little pig goes oink, oink, oink,
   My little dog goes arf, arf, arf,
   My little cat goes meow, meow, meow,
   My little rooster goes cock-a-doodle doo, dee doodle dee
       doodle dee doodle dee doo.

5. I bought me a sheep, *etc*.
   My little sheep goes baa, baa, baa,
   My little pig goes oink, oink, oink,
   My little dog goes arf, arf, arf,
   My little cat goes meow, meow, meow,
   My little rooster goes cock-a-doodle doo, dee doodle dee
       doodle dee doodle dee doo.

6. I bought me a cow, *etc*.
   My little cow goes moo, moo, moo,
   My little sheep goes baa, baa, baa,
   My little pig goes oink, oink, oink,
   My little dog goes arf, arf, arf,
   My little cat goes meow, meow, meow,
   My little rooster goes cock-a-doodle doo, dee doodle dee
       doodle dee doodle dee doo.

THREE LITTLE PIGGIES

A traditional American folk song with a wise moral for all pigs and children.

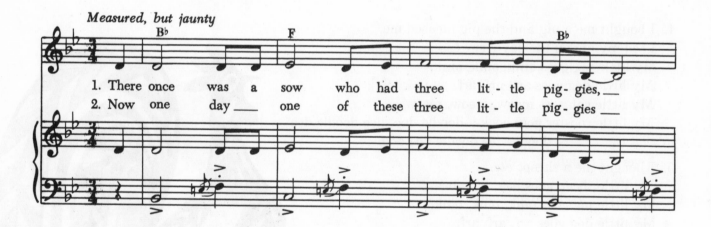

Measured, but jaunty

1. There once was a sow who had three lit-tle pig-gies,___
2. Now one day___ one of these three lit-tle pig-gies___

Three lit-tle pig-gies had she,___
Said to his broth-ers, said he,___

50

And the old sow al - ways went "oink, oink, oink,"
"Why don't we al - ways go 'oink, oink, oink,'

While the pig - gies ____ went ____ "whee, whee, whee." _____
It's so child- ish ___ to go _____ 'whee, whee, whee.'" _____

*snort

3. Now these three piggies grew skinny and lean,
   And skinny they well might be,
   For they always tried to go "oink, oink, oink,"
   When they should have gone "whee, whee, whee."

4. And these three piggies they up and they died,
   A very sad sight to see,
   So don't ever try to go "oink, oink, oink,"
   When you ought to go "whee, whee, whee."

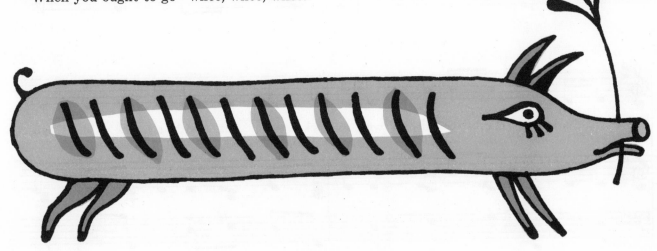

STOP YOUR GROANING

A student song of Afrikaans origin. The Stellenbosch boys are simply boys from the University of Stellenbosch, which is surrounded by mountains and often bothered by bands of baboons. The name of any other school may be substituted for "Stellenbosch" or even the names of children.

The ba - boon climbs the hill with a sick - le tail, with a sick - le tail,

The ba - boon climbs the hill with a sick - le tail, with a sick - le tail,

And the farm-er watch-es till he has come much near-er still,

Then he'll catch him by his lit-tle sick-le tail.

Stop your groan - ing, stop your moan - ing, The Stel-len-bos-se boys are here,

Stop your groan - ing, stop your moan - ing, The Stel-len-bos-se boys are here.

53

BINGO

*Children were singing and spelling out this song about
the dog named Bingo long before the invention of the game of that name.
The first Bingo came from England or Scotland, where
his name may have been a contraction of "bandog," a mastiff watchdog.*

There was a farm-er had a dog And Bing-o was his name-o,

B - I - N - G - O, B - I - N - G - O,

B - I - N - G - O, And Bing-o was his name - o.

54

OLD BLUE

A quiet, sentimental tall story about a good hunting dog.

Smoothly

1. I had a dog and his name was Blue,
2. I chased a possum up a 'sim - mon tree,

And I bet you five dol - lars he's a good dog too.
Blue __ looked __ at pos - sum, pos- sum looked at me.

Sing- ing, "Here, Blue, You're a good dog, you."
Sing- ing, "Here, Blue, You can have some too."

LITTLE WHITE DUCK

*Everyone is glad to be himself in this catchy song, and yet it
still has a sad ending. The music was written by Walt Barrows,
and the words by Bernard Zaritzky.*

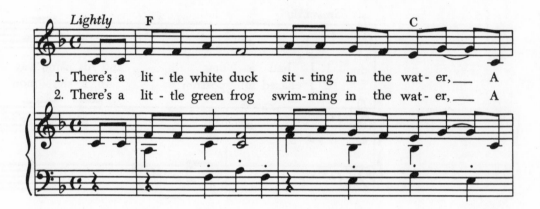

1. There's a lit-tle white duck sit-ting in the wat-er,___ A
2. There's a lit-tle green frog swim-ming in the wat-er,___ A

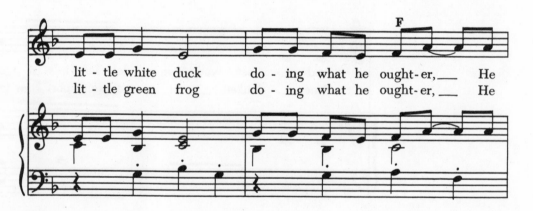

lit-tle white duck do-ing what he ought-er,___ He
lit-tle green frog do-ing what he ought-er,___ He

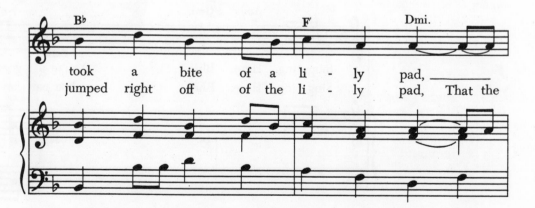

took a bite of a li-ly pad,___
jumped right off of the li-ly pad, That the

Flapped __ his wings and he said, "I'm glad I'm a
lit-tle duck bit and he said, "I'm glad I'm a

lit-tle white duck sit-ting in the wat-er, __ Quack! Quack! Quack!"
lit-tle green frog swim-ming in the wat-er, __ Glug! Glug! Glug!"

3. There's a little black bug floating on the water,
A little black bug doing what he oughter,
He tickled the frog on the lily pad,
That the little duck bit and he said, "I'm glad
I'm a little black bug floating on the water.
Bzz! Bzz! Bzz!"

4. There's a little red snake playing in the water,
A little red snake doing what he oughter,
He frightened the duck and the frog so bad,
He ate the bug and he said, "I'm glad
I'm a little red snake playing in the water.
Hiss! Hiss! Hiss!"

5. Now there's nobody left sitting in the water,
Nobody left doing what he oughter,
There's nothing left but the lily pad,
The duck and the frog ran away; I'm sad
'Cause there's nobody left sitting in the water.
Boo! Hoo! Hoo!

57

MISTER FROG WENT A-COURTING

This song has been consistently popular for more than four centuries.
Hundreds of versions exist, but this one is probably the best known.

Playfully

1. Mis - ter Frog went a - court - ing, he did ride. Ah - hah, ah - hah.
2. He rode up to Miss Mous - ie's den. Ah - hah, ah - hah.

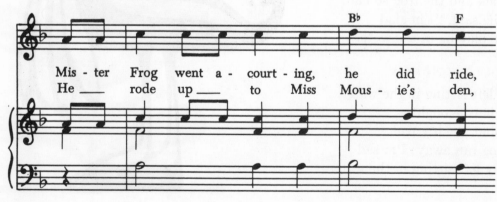

Mis - ter Frog went a - court - ing, he did ride,
He rode up to Miss Mous - ie's den,

58

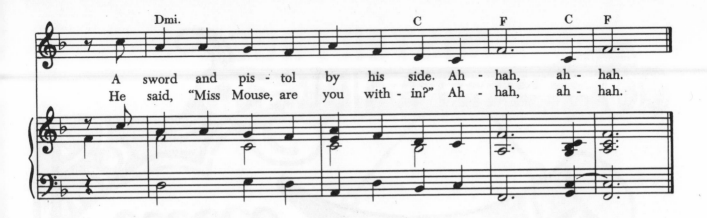

A sword and pis - tol by his side. Ah - hah, ah - hah.
He said, "Miss Mouse, are you with - in?" Ah - hah, ah - hah.

3. He took Miss Mousie on his knee. Ah-hah, ah-hah.
   He took Miss Mousie on his knee,
   He said, "Miss Mouse, will you marry me?" Ah-hah, ah-hah.

4. "Without my Uncle Rat's consent?" Ah-hah, ah-hah.
   "Without my Uncle Rat's consent,
   I wouldn't marry the President." Ah-hah, ah-hah.

5. Uncle Rat laughed and shook his fat sides. Ah-hah, ah-hah.
   Uncle Rat laughed and shook his fat sides,
   To think his niece would be a bride. Ah-hah, ah-hah.

6. "Where will the wedding supper be?" Ah-hah, ah-hah.
   "Where will the wedding supper be?"
   "Away down yonder in a hollow tree." Ah-hah, ah-hah.

7. "What will the wedding supper be?" Ah-hah, ah-hah.
   "What will the wedding supper be?"
   "Two old beans and a black-eyed pea." Ah-hah, ah-hah.

8. They all went sailing on the lake. Ah-hah, ah-hah.
   They all went sailing on the lake,
   They all were swallowed by a big black snake. Ah-hah, ah-hah.

9. So that's the end of one, two, three. Ah-hah, ah-hah.
   So that's the end of one, two, three,
   The Rat, the Frog and Miss Mousie. Ah-hah, ah-hah.

THE FOX & THE GOOSE

[FUCHS, DU HAST DIE GANS GESTOHLEN]

In American folklore, the fox outsmarts everyone and has a jolly feast with his wife and little ones. The German fox may get the goose, but he gets a blood-and-thunder lecture as well.

Bouncy

1. Fox, you stole our goose last night, You picked the fat-test one,
1. *Fuchs, du hast die Gans ge-stoh-len, Gib sie wie-der her,*

Picked the fat-test one,
Gib sie wie-der her,

Now the hunt-er's gone to get you With his horse and gun-gun-gun,
Sonst wird dich der Jä-ger ho-len Mit dem Schiess-ge-wehr, _____

Now the hunt-er's gone to get you With his horse and gun.
Sonst wird dich der Jä-ger ho-len Mit dem Schiess-ge-wehr.

2. Fox, you're running, clipper, clopper,
Think you'll get away?
Think you'll get away?
Bang-bang-bang the gun will sing,
An awful price to pay-pay-pay,
Bang-bang-bang the gun will sing,
An awful price to pay.

3. So, dear fox, when fortune knocks
And plump, round geese you spy,
Plump, round geese you spy,
Let them go — it's best, you know,
Fill up on field mouse pie-pie-pie.
Let them go — it's best, you know,
Fill up on field mouse pie.

2. *Eine grosse lange Flinte*
Schiesst auf dich den Schrot,
Schiesst auf dich den Schrot,
Dass dich färbt die rote Tinte,
Und dann bist du tot,
Dass dich färbt die rote Tinte,
Und dann bist du tot.

3. *Liebes Füchslein, lass dir raten,*
Sei doch nur kein Dieb,
Sei doch nur kein Dieb,
Nimm, du brauchst nicht Gänsebraten,
Mit der Maus vorlieb,
Nimm, du brauchst nicht Gänsebraten,
Mit der Maus vorlieb.

THE CAPTURED BIRD

[POYMANAYA PTEECHKA]

A favorite Russian children's song is this dialogue between a bird and the
well-meaning but misguided child who caught it in his net.

Moderately, flowing

1. Pret - ty bird, I've got you now, Though you're quick and clev - er,
1. A pa - pa - las pteech - ka, stoy, Nye uy - dyosh eez sye - tee,

You flew right in - to my net, Now you're mine for - ev - er.
Nye raz - ta - nem - sya sta - boy, Nee za shto na svyet - ye.

Oh, what good am I to you? Let me go I pray you,
Akh, za - chem, za - chem ya vam, Mee - len - kee - ya dye - tee?

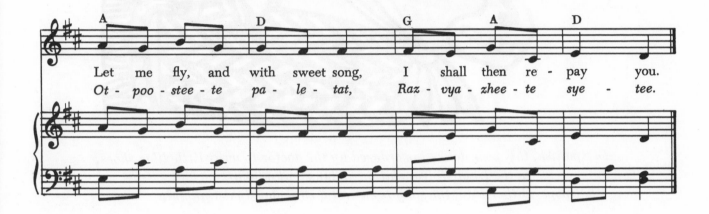

Let me fly, and with sweet song, I shall then re - pay you.
Ot - poo - stee - te pa - le - tat, Raz - vya - zhee - te sye - tee.

2. Pretty bird, I'll give to you
   Sugarplums and candy,
   I will always care for you,
   Life will be so dandy.

You may think you love me well,
But you'll bring me sorrow,
If I ate your sugarplums,
I would die tomorrow.

2. *Pteechka, pteechka! Kak lyoobeet,*
   Mi tyebya bi stalee,
   Nye rozvoleeleeb groosteet,
   Vsyob tyebya laskalee.

Vyeryoo, dyetkee, no dlya nas,
Vrednee vasha laskee,
S nyeekh zakreela bi kak raz,
Ya na vyekee glaskee.

MY DONKEY

[MI BURRO]

*In Spanish, this poor donkey is ordered by the doctor to wear little lilac shoes;
in the English translation he must eat a lot of
lollipops. Either way, the song is entirely, ridiculously delightful.*

Flowing

1. Oh my don - key, my don - key, His head aches, so up - on it
1. A mi bur - ro, a mi bur - ro Le due - le la ca - be - za,

The doc - tor has told him To wear a wool - en bon - net.
El mé - di - co le ha pues - to Un - a gor - ri - ta ne - gra.

Repeat only for second verse

To wear a wool-en bon-net? To wear a wool-en bon-net,

Un - a gor - ri - ta ne - gra? Un - a gor - ri - ta neg - ra.

And eat a lot of lol-li-pops, a lot of lol-li-pops.

Za - pa - ti - tos li - la - la - la, za - pa - ti - tos li - la.

2. Oh my donkey, his throat hurts,
And how he was astounded,
The doctor has told him
To wear a scarf around it.
To wear a scarf around it? To wear a scarf around it.
To wear a woolen bonnet? To wear a woolen bonnet.
And eat a lot of lollipops, a lot of lollipops.

2. *A mi burro, a mi burro*
   Le duele la garganta,
   El médico le ha puesto
   Una bufanda blanca.
Una bufanda blanca? Una bufanda blanca.
Una gorrita negra? Una gorrita negra.
Zapatitos lila-la-la, zapatitos lila.

CUCKOO

*The cuckoo of this song is not the traditional bird who brings glad
tidings, tells no lies and sweetly sings of love — not at all!*

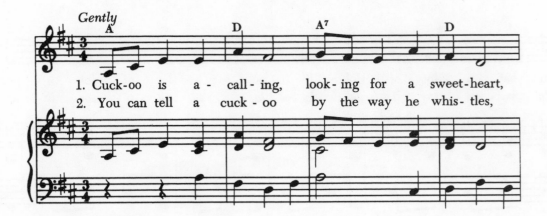

1. Cuck-oo is a - call - ing, look - ing for a sweet-heart,
2. You can tell a cuck - oo by the way he whis - tles,

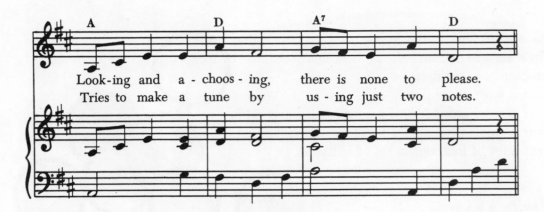

Look-ing and a - choos - ing, there is none to please.
Tries to make a tune by us - ing just two notes.

Cuck - oo, cuck - oo, ah, _____ ah, _____

(optional)

66

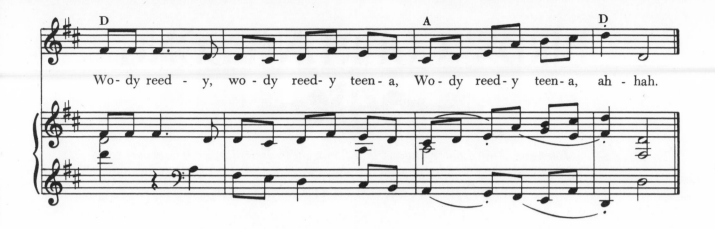

Wo-dy reed-y, wo-dy reed-y teen-a, Wo-dy reed-y teen-a, ah-hah.

3. Cuckoo says he's wealthy: "Look at my fine clothing,
   Look at this fine jacket!" What a stupid bird!   (*Chorus*)

4. The one I love has more than you can ever hope for.
   What's he got that I lack? Love, dear cuckoo, love.   (*Chorus*)

CHORUS:

   Cuckoo, cuckoo, ah, ah,
   Wody reedy, wody reedy, teena,
   Wody reedy, teena, ah-hah.

BIRDS' COURTING SONG

John and Alan Lomax suggest that this song is derived from Chaucer's
The Parliament of Fowls. Some twenty birds speak in the old English ballad,
but only four are known in most American versions.

Softly

1. "Hi!" said the black-bird sit-ting on a chair. "Once I court-ed a la-dy fair;
2. "Hi!" said the lit-tle leath-er-wing'd bat. "I will tell you the rea-son that,

She proved fick-le and turned her __ back, And e-ver since then I've dressed in black."
Rea-son that __ I fly in the night: Be-cause __ I've lost my heart's de-light."

3. "Hi!" said the little mourning dove,
   "I'll tell you how to gain her love,
   Court her night and court her day,
   Never give her time to say 'O nay.'"

4. "Hi!" said the woodpecker, sitting on a fence.
   "Once I courted a handsome wench,
   She got sulky and from me fled,
   And ever since then my head's been red."

GO TELL AUNT RHODY

Aunt Rhody in the North, Aunt Patsy in the South,
or Aunt Nancy in the West, she always loses her valuable gray goose
in one of America's best known folk songs.

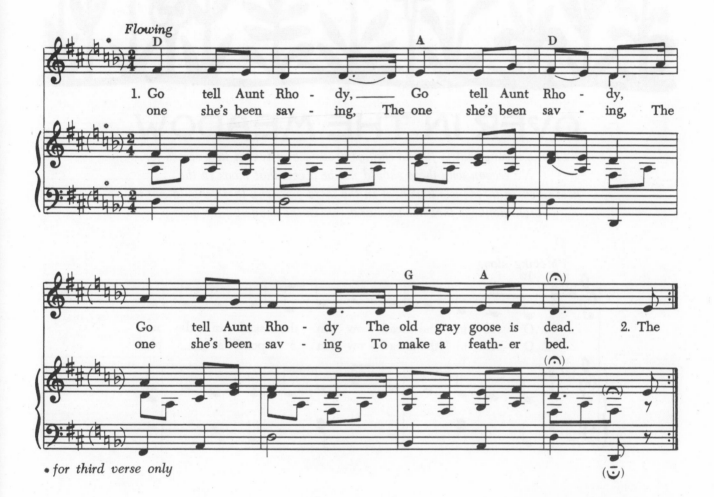

1. Go tell Aunt Rho - dy, ____ Go tell Aunt Rho - dy,
   one she's been sav - ing, The one she's been sav - ing, The

Go tell Aunt Rho - dy The old gray goose is dead. 2. The
one she's been sav - ing To make a feath- er bed.

*for third verse only

3. She died in the millpond,
   She died in the millpond,
   She died in the millpond
   Standing on her head.

4. The goslings are crying,
   The goslings are crying,
   The goslings are crying
   Because their mammy's dead.

5. Go tell Aunt Rhody,
   Go tell Aunt Rhody,
   Go tell Aunt Rhody
   The old gray goose is dead.

69

OVER IN THE MEADOW

This is a song that is fun to change around and invent new verses for.
No reason why there should not be a cow that moos in the
first verse, or three owls that hoot in the third—or why there should not be
eight donkeys that hee-haw and live in the shade by the gate.

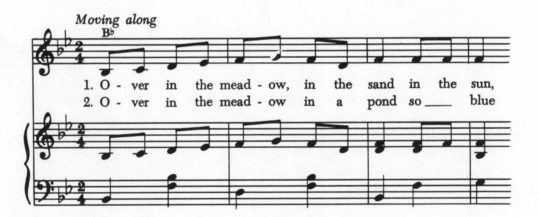

1. O - ver in the mead - ow, in the sand in the sun,
2. O - ver in the mead - ow in a pond so ___ blue

Lived an old __ moth - er frog __ and her lit - tle frog - gie one.
Lived an old __ moth - er duck __ and her lit - tle ducks __ two.

"Croak!" said the moth-er;—— "I croak," said the one,
"Quack!" said the moth-er;—— "we quack," said the two,

So they croaked and were glad in the sand in the sun.
So they quacked and were glad in the pond so —— blue.

3. Over in the meadow, in a hole in a tree,
   Lived an old mother bluebird and her little birdies three,
   "Tweet!" said the mother; "we tweet," said the three,
   So they sang and were glad in the hole in the tree.

4. Over in the meadow on a rock by the shore
   Lived an old mother snake and her little snakes four,
   "Hiss!" said the mother; "we hiss," said the four,
   So they hissed and were glad on the rock by the shore.

5. Over in the meadow, in a big beehive,
   Lived an old mother bee and her little bees five,
   "Buzz!" said the mother; "we buzz," said the five,
   So they buzzed and were glad in the big beehive.

SONG OF THE FISHES

The fish take over the boat in this whimsical sea song,
but its New England origin can be seen in the no-nonsense last verse.

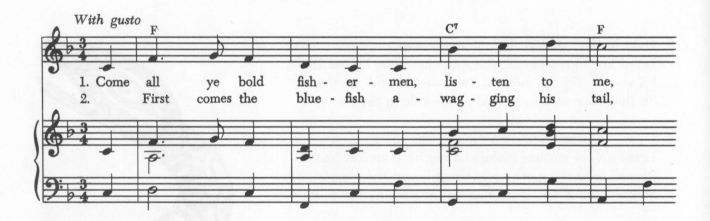

1. Come all ye bold fish-er-men, lis-ten to me,
2. First comes the blue-fish a-wag-ging his tail,

I'll sing you a song of the fish in the sea.
He comes up on deck and yells, "All hands make sail!"

Chorus:

So blow ye winds west - er - ly, west - er - ly blow, ___

We're bound ___ to the south - ward, so stead - y we go.

3. Next come the eels with their nimble tails,
   They jump up aloft and loose all the sails.   (*Chorus*)

4. Then comes the mackerel with his striped back,
   He flops on the bridge and yells, "Board the main tack!"   (*Chorus*)

5. Up jumps the fisherman, stalwart and grim,
   And with his big net he scoops them all in.   (*Chorus*)

CHORUS:

So blow, ye winds, westerly, westerly blow,
We're bound to the southward, so steady we go.

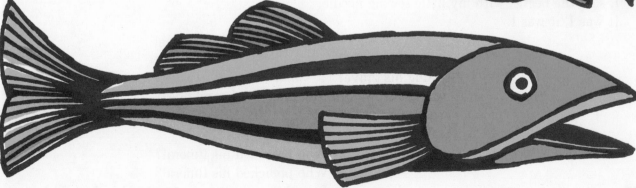

COCKY ROBIN

Some of the most beloved children's songs are not filled with sunshine and roses.
This very old song begins with an inquest and ends with a funeral.

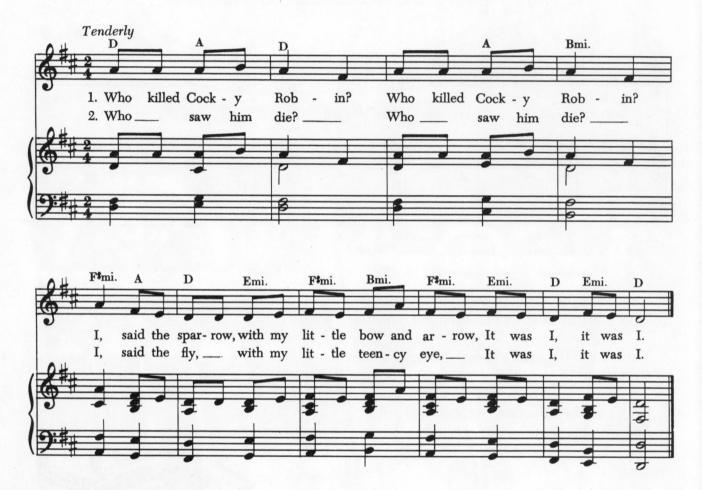

Tenderly

1. Who killed Cock - y Rob - in? Who killed Cock - y Rob - in?
2. Who ___ saw him die? ___ Who ___ saw him die? ___

I, said the spar - row, with my lit - tle bow and ar - row, It was I, it was I.
I, said the fly, ___ with my lit - tle teen - cy eye, ___ It was I, it was I.

3. Who made his shroud?
   Who made his shroud?
   I, said the beetle, with my little sewing needle,
   It was I, it was I.

4. Who dug his grave?
   Who dug his grave?
   I, said the crow, with my little spade and hoe,
   It was I, it was I.

5. Who preached his funeral?
   Who preached his funeral?
   I, said the swallow, just as loud as I could holler,
   It was I, it was I.

MARY HAD A LITTLE LAMB

This simple little song, written in 1830 by Mrs. Sarah Joseph Hale of Boston,
is probably the best-known jingle in the English language.

1. Ma - ry had a lit - tle lamb, lit - tle lamb, lit - tle lamb,
2. And ev' - ry-where that Ma - ry went, Ma - ry went, Ma - ry went,

Ma - ry had a lit - tle lamb, its fleece was white as snow.
Ev' - ry-where that Ma - ry went the lamb was sure to go.

3. It followed her to school one day, school one day, school one day,
   It followed her to school one day, which was against the rules.

4. It made the children laugh and play, laugh and play, laugh and play,
   It made the children laugh and play to see a lamb at school.

THERE WAS AN OLD WOMAN

The tune of this beloved English nursery rhyme is the historical Irish air
"Lilliburlero," which was sung in the seventeenth-century
Irish wars, though with more belligerent words.

There was an old wo - man tossed up in a bas - ket,
And where she was go - ing I could - n't but ask it,

Sev - en - teen times as high as the moon.
For in her hand she car - ried a broom.

"Old wo - man, old wo - man, old wo - man," said I,

"Oh whith - er, oh whith - er, oh whith - er so high?"

"To sweep— the cob - webs off — the sky." ——

"Shall I go with you?" "Aye, bye and bye."

79

THE MAILMAN

[POČTOVSKY PANÁČEK]

*Country mailmen in Czechoslovakia used to blow on horns
to announce their arrival. This song about such a mailman is a great favorite with Czech children.*

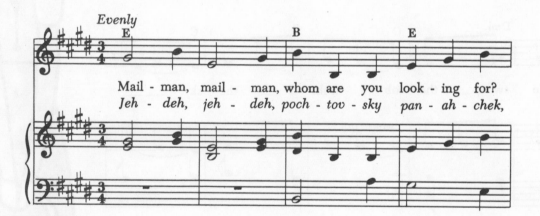

Evenly

Mail - man, mail - man, whom are you look - ing for?
Jeh - deh, jeh - deh, poch - tov - sky pan - ah - chek,

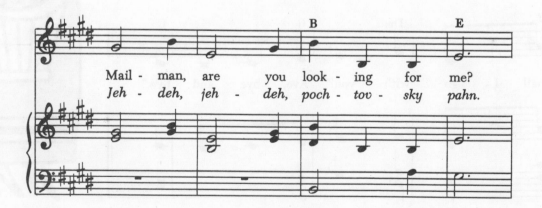

Mail - man, are you look - ing for me?
Jeh - deh, jeh - deh, poch - tov - sky pahn.

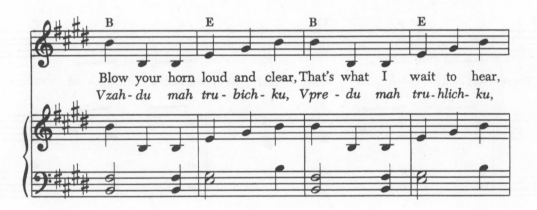

Blow your horn loud and clear, That's what I wait to hear,
Vzah - du mah tru - bich - ku, Vpre - du mah tru - hlich - ku,

Hope you've brought a let - ter for me.
Jeh - deh, jeh - deh, poch - tov - sky pahn.

THERE WAS A CROOKED MAN

*It can be fun to assume the most complicated and crooked postures
while singing or listening to this song.*

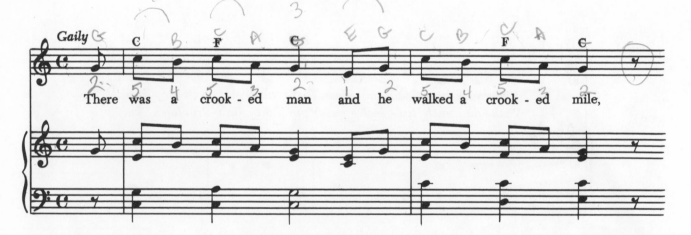

There was a crook-ed man and he walked a crook-ed mile,

He found a crook-ed six-pence up-on a crook-ed stile.

He bought a crook-ed cat which caught a crook-ed mouse,

And they all lived to-geth-er in a lit-tle crook-ed house.

TWINKLE, TWINKLE, LITTLE STAR

The Mad Hatter's parody of this old rhyme by Jane Taylor in Alice in Wonderland
is almost as widely known as the original, and we have included it as the second verse.
The tune has been used by many composers and the
arrangement here, with minor changes, was written by Mozart around 1778.

1. Twink-le, twink-le, lit-tle star, How I won-der what you are.
2. Twink-le, twink-le, lit-tle bat, How I won-der what you're at.

Up a-bove the world so high, Like a dia-mond in the sky,
Up a-bove the world you fly, Like a tea tray in the sky.

Twink-le, twink-le, lit-tle star, How I won-der what you are.
Twink-le, twink-le, lit-tle bat, How I won-der what you're at.

THIS OLD MAN

A popular number-learning song. The chorus is usually accompanied by clapping, stamping, banging or drumming of some sort or other.

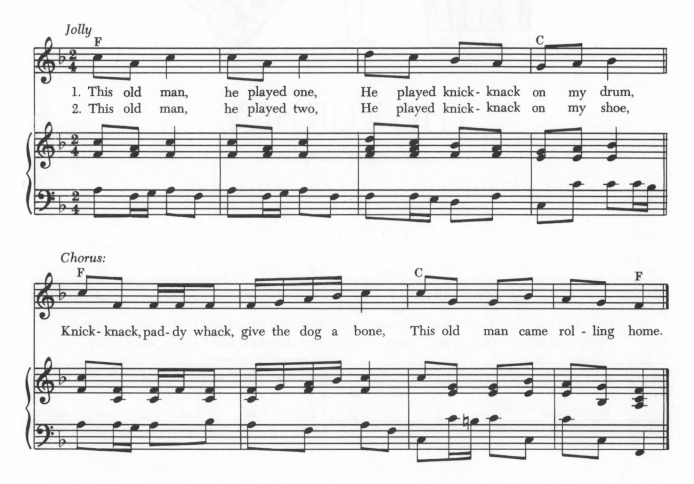

Jolly

1. This old man, he played one, He played knick-knack on my drum,
2. This old man, he played two, He played knick-knack on my shoe,

Chorus:

Knick-knack, pad-dy whack, give the dog a bone, This old man came rol-ling home.

3. This old man, he played three,
   He played knick-knack on my knee.
   (Chorus)
4. This old man, he played four,
   He played knick-knack on my door.
   (Chorus)
5. This old man, he played five,
   He played knick-knack on my hive.
   (Chorus)
6. This old man, he played six,
   He played knick-knack on my sticks.
   (Chorus)

7. This old man, he played seven,
   He played knick-knack up to heaven.
   (Chorus)
8. This old man, he played eight,
   He played knick-knack at the gate.
   (Chorus)
9. This old man, he played nine,
   He played knick-knack on my line.
   (Chorus)
10. This old man, he played ten,
    He played knick-knack over again.
    (Chorus)

CHORUS: With a knick-knack, paddy whack, give the dog a bone,
   This old man came rolling home.

THE TURKEY

[DEBRECZENBE KENE MENNI]

A Hungarian children's song. Béla Bartók used this tune
as the basis for one of his piano pieces.

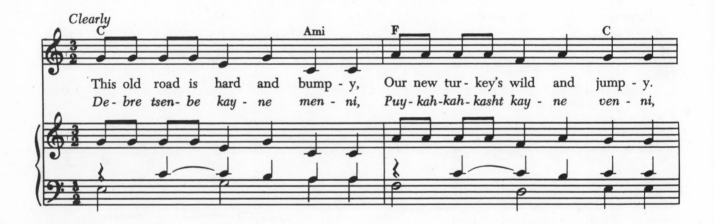

This old road is hard and bump-y, Our new tur-key's wild and jump-y.
De - bre tsen- be kay - ne men - ni, Puy-kah-kah-kasht kay - ne ven - ni,

Driv - er! Driv - er! Not so jerk - y! Or you'll make us lose our tur - key.
Vee - dyaz ko-cheesh yu-kash a kash, Kee- eh - shik a puy-kah-kah-kash.

BOBBY SHAFTO

*When young, handsome, blond Robert Shafto of Whitworth ran for
Parliament in 1761, this song was widely sung by his supporters.*

Simply

1. Bob - by Shaf - to went to sea, Sil - ver buck - les on his knee,
2. Bob - by Shaf - to's fat and fair, Comb - ing down his yel - low hair,

He'll come back and mar - ry me, ___ Pret - ty Bob - by Shaf - to.
He's my love for ev - er - more, ___ Pret - ty Bob - by Shaf - to.

JACK AND JILL

*Various origin theories drag Jack and Jill back into ancient mystic rituals
and old Norse mythology, but nothing has been proved except
the tremendous popularity of this nursery song.*

Jack and Jill went up the hill To fetch a pail of wa - ter,

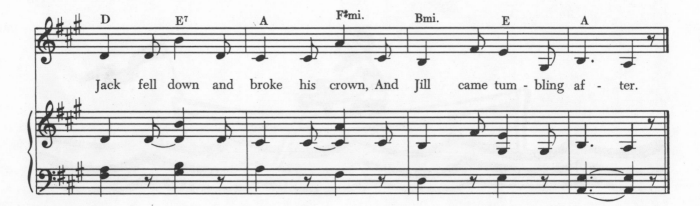

Jack fell down and broke his crown, And Jill came tum - bling af - ter.

LITTLE SACKA SUGAR

*Woody Guthrie wrote many children's songs and this is one of the
most beloved—full of jazzy rhythms, repetition and nonsense.
It is often sung to a child as he is being jiggled and tickled on a grownup's knee.*

Jig - gle, jig - gle, jig - gle, jig- gle, Tick - le, tick - le, tick - le,

Lit - tle sack - a sug - ar, I could eat you up.

Jig - gle, jig - gle, jig - gle, jig- gle, Pick - le, pick - le, pick - le,

**It is not necessary to be conscientious enough to play all the
repeated sixteenth notes in the right hand.*

Lit - tle sack - a sug - ar, I could eat you up.

1. Hey, hey, hey, my lit - tle sack - a sug - ar,
2. Hey, hey, hey, my lit - tle hon - ey - bun - ny,

Ho, ho, ho, my lit - tle sack - a sweets,
Ho, ho, ho, my lit - tle tur - tle dove,

Hee, hee, hee, my pret - ty lit - tle an - gel, So
Hee, hee, hee, my lit - tle sack - a 'ta - ters, So

pret - ty,   pret - ty,   pret - ty,   I   could eat   your feet.
pret - ty,   pret - ty,   pret - ty,   I   could eat   your toes.

D. C. al FINE

Repeat chorus after each stanza.

3. Hey, hey, hey, my tootsie-wootsie,
   Rangle, tangle, dangle, and a honey and a tree,
   Ho, ho, ho, my butterfly flitters,
   So pretty, pretty, pretty, I could eat your nose.   *(Chorus)*

4. Dribble, dribble, dribble, a coo and a cuddle,
   Kick your foot like a bicycle pedal,
   Pretty little hoot owl and a one-eyed frog,
   Pretty, pretty, pretty, I could gobble you whole.   *(Chorus)*

CHORUS:

   Jiggle, jiggle, jiggle, jiggle,
   Tickle, tickle, tickle,
   Little sacka sugar, I could eat you up.
   Jiggle, jiggle, jiggle, jiggle,
   Pickle, pickle, pickle,
   Little sacka sugar, I could eat you up.

EENCY WEENCY SPIDER

*A well-known finger-play song. The index fingers and thumbs indicate
the spider's motion, and appropriate hand gestures act out the rest of the song.*

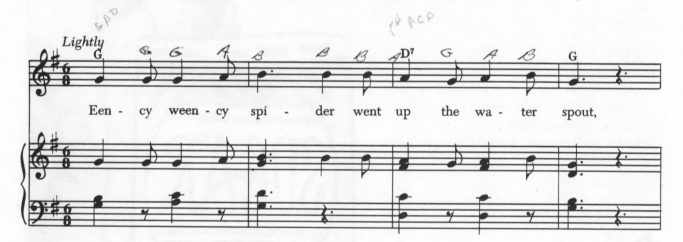

Een - cy ween - cy spi - der went up the wa - ter spout,

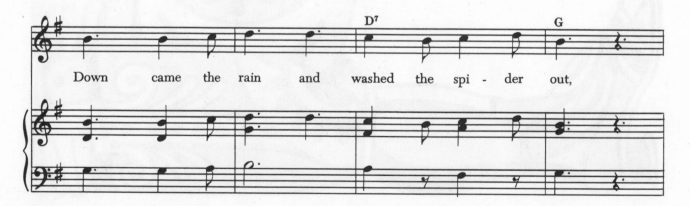

Down came the rain and washed the spi - der out,

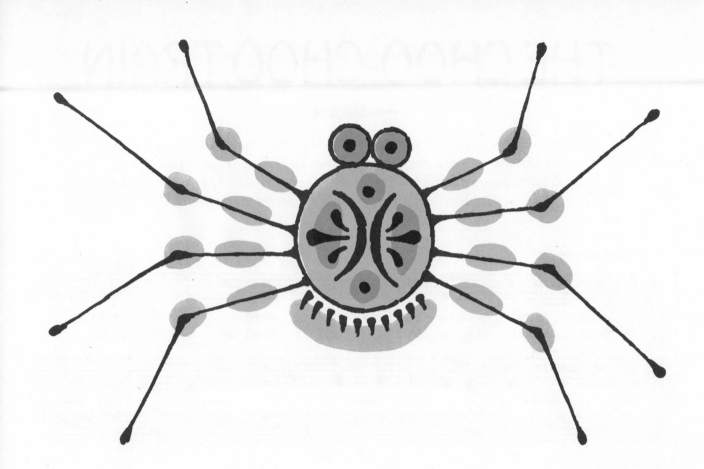

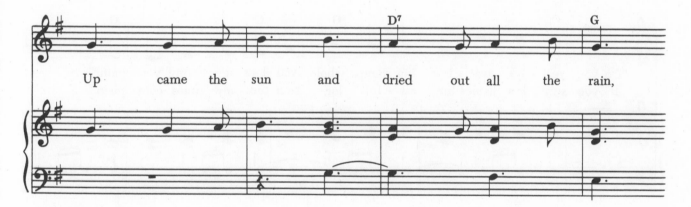

Up came the sun and dried out all the rain,

So the een - cy ween - cy spi - der went up the spout a - gain.

THE CHOO-CHOO TRAIN

In this song, the train gives a reassuring answer to some probing questions.
For the best effect, a deep-voiced grownup is needed for the chorus,
or children may sing it an octave higher than written. The words are by
Hal David and the music by Norman Monath.

1. "What do you do with the big black coal?" I asked the rail-road train.
2. "What do you do when the fire is hot?" I asked the rail-road train.

"Do you real-ly swal-low big lumps whole, And does it bring you pain?"
"If you swal-low flames an aw-ful lot, Your tum-my must com-plain."

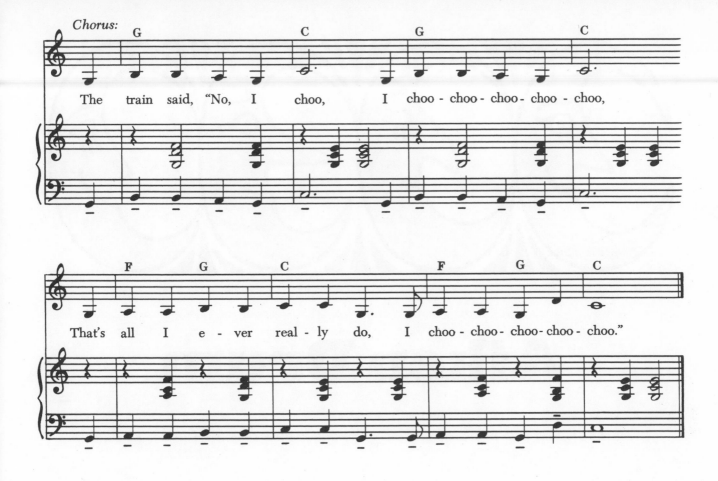

Chorus:

The train said, "No, I choo, I choo-choo-choo-choo-choo, That's all I e-ver real-ly do, I choo-choo-choo-choo-choo."

3. "What do you do with the big black smoke?"
   I asked the railroad train.
   "Do you swallow smoke until you choke?
   I wish you would explain."   (*Chorus*)

CHORUS:

The train said, "No, I choo,
I choo-choo-choo-choo-choo,
That's all I ever really do,
I choo-choo-choo-choo-choo."

Aiken Drum

A real ladle to bang with in accompaniment makes this Scottish song irresistible to all children.

1. There __ was a man lived in the moon, lived in the moon, lived in the moon,
2. And his hat was made of good cream cheese, of good cream cheese, of good cream cheese,

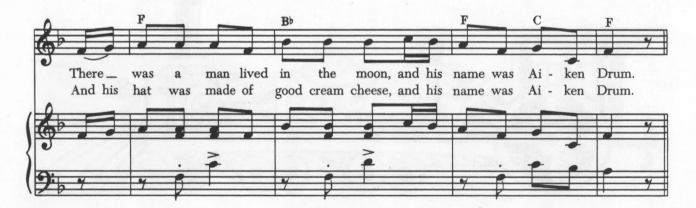

There __ was a man lived in the moon, and his name was Ai - ken Drum.
And his hat was made of good cream cheese, and his name was Ai - ken Drum.

And he played up-on a la-dle, a la-dle, a la-dle,

And he played up-on a la-dle, and his name was Ai-ken Drum.

3. And his coat was made of good roast beef,
   of good roast beef, of good roast beef,
   And his coat was made of good roast beef,
   and his name was Aiken Drum.   (*Chorus*)

4. And his buttons made of penny loaves,
   of penny loaves, of penny loaves,
   And his buttons made of penny loaves,
   and his name was Aiken Drum.   (*Chorus*)

5. And his breeches made of haggis bags,
   of haggis bags, of haggis bags,
   And his breeches made of haggis bags,
   and his name was Aiken Drum.   (*Chorus*)

CHORUS:

   And he played upon a ladle, a ladle, a ladle,
   And he played upon a ladle, and his name was Aiken Drum.

COCK-A-DOODLE-DOO!

This was a very popular nursery rhyme three-and-a-half centuries ago,
and remains just as popular to this day.

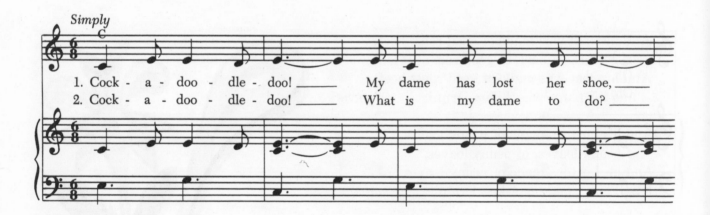

1. Cock - a - doo - dle - doo! _____ My dame has lost her shoe, _____
2. Cock - a - doo - dle - doo! _____ What is my dame to do? _____

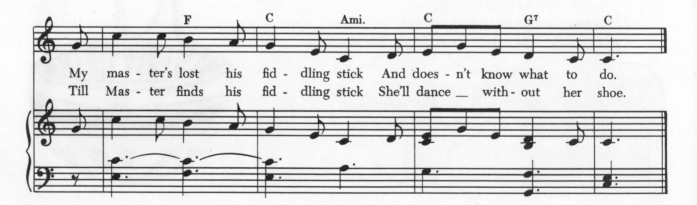

My mas - ter's lost his fid - dling stick And does - n't know what to do.
Till Mas - ter finds his fid - dling stick She'll dance _ with - out her shoe.

THE MUFFIN MAN

*A hundred years ago in England children waited for the Muffin Man
to come around with his wares as children today wait for the Ice Cream Man.*

Bouncy — F — Gmi. — G⁷ — C

1. Oh, do you know the muf-fin man, the muf-fin man, the muf-fin man,
2. Oh yes, I know the muf-fin man, the muf-fin man, the muf-fin man,

F — Gmi. — C — F

Oh, do you know the muf-fin man that lives in Dru-ry Lane?
Oh yes, I know the muf-fin man that lives in Dru-ry Lane.

POP! GOES THE WEASEL

A great favorite of children everywhere.
The louder the "Pop!" the better children like it.

That's the way the mo - ney goes, Pop! Goes the wea - sel.

WHO DID?

A question-and-answer song simple enough for the youngest children to sing without much practice. Older children can make up more verses using other Bible-story characters.

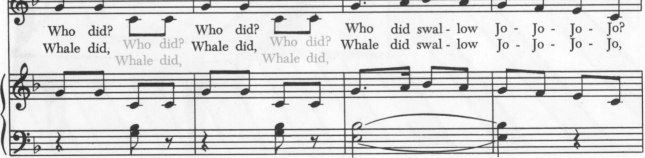

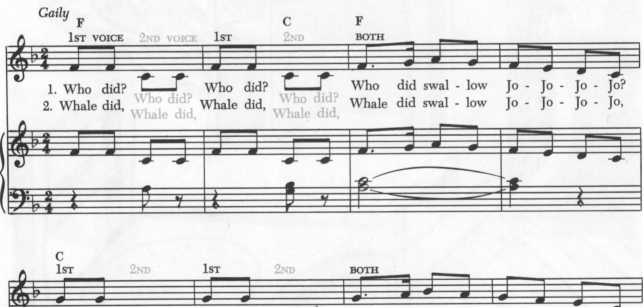

Gaily **F**

1ST VOICE 2ND VOICE 1ST 2ND BOTH

1. Who did? Who did? Who did? Who did? Who did swal-low Jo-Jo-Jo-Jo?
2. Whale did, Who did? Whale did, Who did? Whale did swal-low Jo-Jo-Jo-Jo,
   Whale did, Whale did,

C

1ST 2ND 1ST 2ND BOTH

Who did? Who did? Who did? Who did? Who did swal-low Jo-Jo-Jo-Jo?
Whale did, Who did? Whale did, Who did? Whale did swal-low Jo-Jo-Jo-Jo,
Whale did, Whale did,

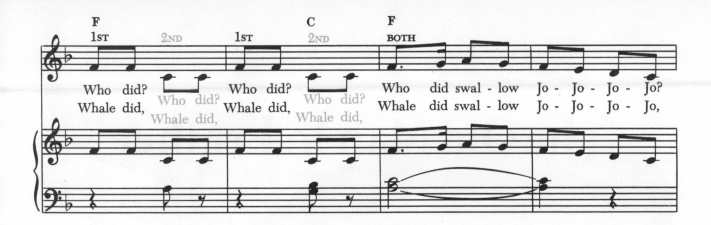

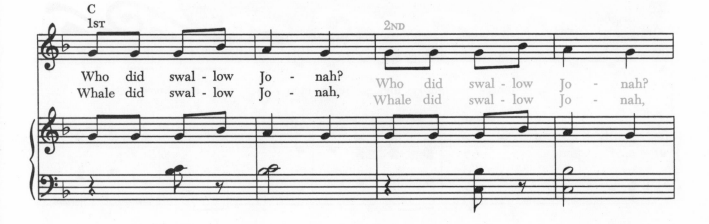

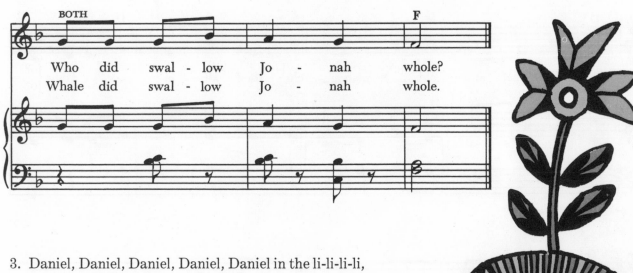

3. Daniel, Daniel, Daniel, Daniel, Daniel in the li-li-li-li,
   Daniel, Daniel, Daniel, Daniel, Daniel in the li-li-li-li,
   Daniel, Daniel, Daniel, Daniel, Daniel in the li-li-li-li,
   Daniel in the lion's, Daniel in the lion's, Daniel in the lion's den.

The Old Man in Leather

This is the first stanza of a 17th-century ballad entitled
"The Wiltshire Wedding Between Daniel Do-Well and Doll the Dairy Maid,
with the Consent of Her Old Father Leather-Coat and her Dear and Tender Mother Plodweli."

One mis-ty, mois-ty morn-ing,— when clou-dy was the wea-ther,—

There I met an old— man— clo-thed all in lea-ther,

Clo-thed all in lea-ther,— with cap un-der his chin.

"How do you do? How do you do? How do you do a-gain, a-gain?"

SIX LITTLE DUCKS

This song is usually accompanied by hand motions:
the proper number of fingers are held up when a number is mentioned,
and the "quack-quack-quack" chorus is accompanied by sturdy arm-flapping in time to the music.

1. Six lit - tle ducks that I once knew, Fat ducks, pret - ty ducks they were too,
2. Down to the mead - ow they would go, Wig - wag, wig-gle- wag, to and fro,

But the one lit - tle duck with the feath - er on his back,
But the one lit - tle duck with the feath - er on his back,

He led the oth - ers with his quack - quack - quack.

Quack-quack-quack, quack-quack-quack, He led the oth - ers with his quack- quack- quack.

THE LITTLE NUT TREE

It has been suggested that this lovely old song refers to the visit of
Juana of Castile, the King of Spain's mad daughter, to the court of Henry VII in 1506.

I had a lit-tle nut tree, noth-ing would it bear,

But a sil-ver nut-meg and a gold-en pear.

The King of Spain's daugh-ter came to vi-sit me,

And all ____ for the sake of my lit - tle nut tree.

WHERE'S MISTER THUMBKIN?

*Sung to the tune of "Frère Jacques," this is one of the many finger-play songs beloved of babies
and small children. Each thumb in turn is held up at "Here I am. Here I am,"
wriggled in turn at "How are you this morning? Very well, I thank you."
Each hand takes refuge behind the back at the words "Run and hide." The same motions are then
repeated for each finger of the hand: Pointer, Middleman, Ringman and Pinky.*

Where's Mis-ter Thumb-kin? Where's Mis-ter Thumb-kin? Here I am. Here I am.

How are you this morn-ing? Ve-ry well, I thank you. Run and hide. Run and hide.

Lloyd George Knew My Father

A song of few words, said to have been inspired by the appointment of a coal-miner's son as Prime Minister of England, set to the refrain of Sir Arthur Sullivan's familiar hymn, "Onward, Christian Soldiers."

Lloyd George knew my fa - ther, __ Fa - ther knew Lloyd George.

With fervor

Lloyd George knew my fa - ther, __ Fa - ther knew Lloyd__ George.

a tempo

Lloyd George knew my fa - ther, Fa - ther knew Lloyd George.

John Brown's Baby

This parody version of "John Brown's Body" is usually played as a pantomime game.

First the song is sung through as it stands. The second time the song is sung, the word "baby" is omitted each time it occurs, and a pantomime of rocking a baby in one's arms is substituted. The third time, the pantomime of rocking a baby continues to replace the word "baby," and in addition the word "cold" is omitted each time it occurs and a sneeze or a cough is substituted. So it progresses up to the last repetition, which goes like this:

John Brown's (rock imaginary baby) had a (sneeze) upon his (tap chest), And they (rub chest) with (hold nose and make wry face).

At each new number do not sing, but make gestures. Piano plays melody throughout.

2. Rock imaginary baby in arms.
3. Sneeze.
4. Point to chest.
5. Rub chest.
6. Hold nose and make wry face.

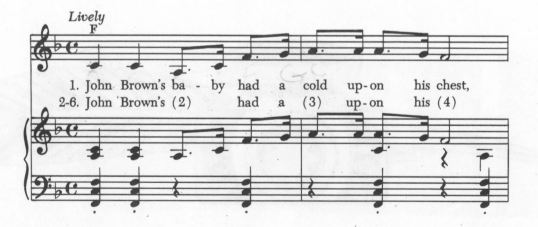

Lively
F

1. John Brown's ba - by had a cold up-on his chest,
2-6. John Brown's (2) had a (3) up-on his (4)

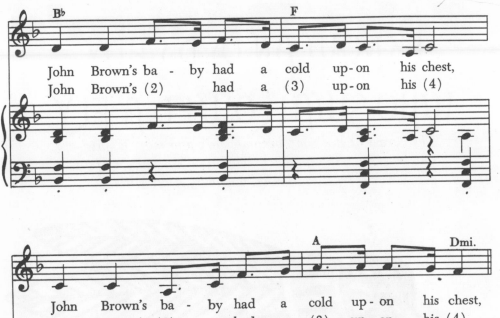

John Brown's ba - by had a cold up - on his chest,
John Brown's (2) had a (3) up - on his (4)

John Brown's ba - by had a cold up - on his chest,
John Brown's (2) had a (3) up - on his (4)

And they rubbed it with cam - phor - a - ted oil.
And they (5) with (6).

115

I KNOW AN OLD LADY
WHO SWALLOWED A FLY

The verses of this song become more and more absurd—
but, somehow, the final sensible line rings silliest of all.
Words by Rose Bonne, music by Alan Mills.

2. I know an old la-dy who swal-lowed a spi-der,

That wrig-gled and jig-gled and tick-led in-side her;

She swal-lowed the spi-der to catch the fly,

I don't know why she swal-lowed the fly. I think she'll die.____

117

3. I know an old la-dy who swal-lowed a bird,
4. I know an old la-dy who swal-lowed a cat, I-

How ab-surd to swal-low a bird.
ma-gine that! She swal-lowed a cat.

Do not repeat for verse 3

(3.cont'd.)She swal-lowed the bird to catch the spi-der, That
(4.cont'd.)She swal-lowed the cat to catch the bird,____ She
swal-lowed the bird to catch the spi-der, That

Repeat for verse 4 and as often as necessary for verses 5, 6, and 7.

wrig-gled and jig-gled and tick-led in-side her;

118

5. I know an old lady who swallowed a dog,
   She was a hog to swallow a dog.
   She swallowed the dog to catch the cat,
   She swallowed the cat to catch the bird,
   She swallowed the bird to catch the spider,
   That wriggled and jiggled and tickled inside her;
   She swallowed the spider to catch the fly,
   I don't know why she swallowed the fly.
   I think she'll die.

6. I know an old lady who swallowed a goat,
   Opened her throat and swallowed a goat.
   She swallowed the goat to catch the dog,
   She swallowed the dog to catch the cat, *etc.*

7. I know an old lady who swallowed a cow,
   I don't know how she swallowed a cow.
   She swallowed the cow to catch the goat,
   She swallowed the goat to catch the dog,
   She swallowed the dog to catch the cat, *etc.*

THERE WAS A MAN AND HE WAS MAD

*An American version of an old English nursery rhyme. Children like to make
up whole new sequences of verses of a more modern nature, for instance:
"There was a man and he was mad, And he jumped onto a launching pad...."*

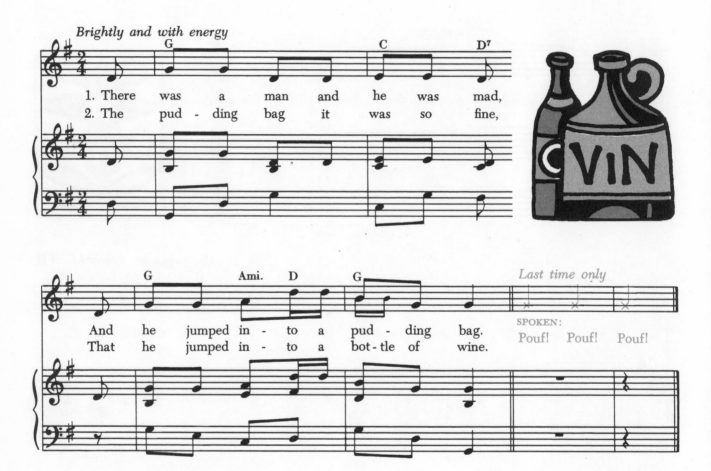

Brightly and with energy

G   C   D7

1. There was a man and he was mad,
2. The pud-ding bag it was so fine,

G   Ami. D   G   *Last time only*

And he jumped in-to a pud-ding bag.   SPOKEN:
That he jumped in-to a bot-tle of wine. Pouf! Pouf! Pouf!

3. The bottle of wine it was so thick,
   That he jumped into a walking stick.

4. The walking stick it was so narrow,
   That he jumped into a wheelbarrow.

5. The wheelbarrow it was so rotten,
   That he jumped into a bag of cotton.

6. The bag of cotton caught on fire,
   And blew him up to Jeremiah!

120

COTTLESTON PIE

Some of the songs that appear in A. A. Milne's children's classic Winnie-the-Pooh were set to music by H. Fraser-Smith. Cottleston Pie, says Milne, is what a bear sings when his brain feels fluffy.

Words by A. A. Milne
Tune by H. Fraser-Smith

Cot - tle - ston, Cot - tle - ston, Cot - tle - ston pie,

A fly ___ can't bird but a bird ___ can fly;

Ask me a rid - dle and I ___ re - ply:

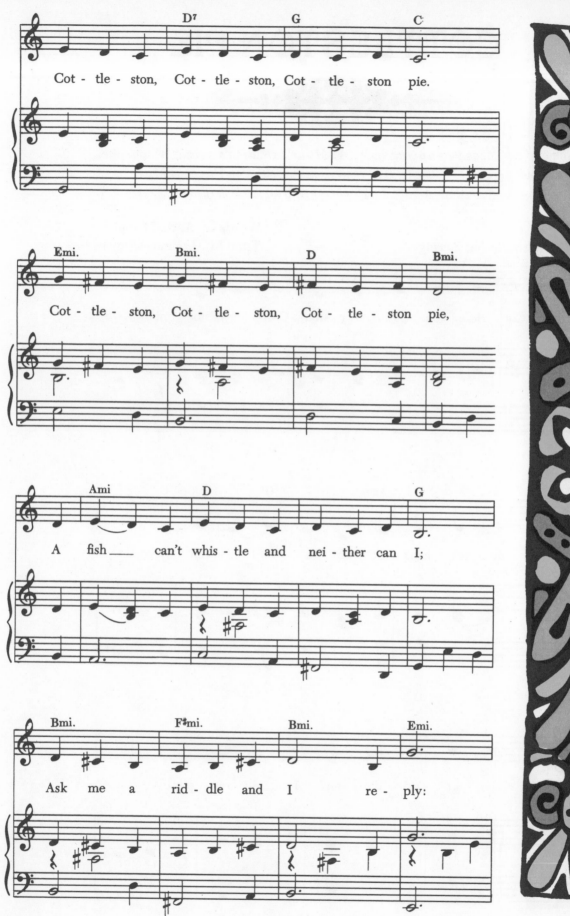

Cot - tle - ston, Cot - tle - ston, Cot - tle - ston pie.

Cot - tle - ston, Cot - tle - ston, Cot - tle - ston pie,

A fish___ can't whis - tle and nei - ther can I;

Ask me a rid - dle and I re - ply:

Cot - tle - ston, Cot - tle - ston, Cot - tle - ston pie.

John Jacob Jingleheimer Schmidt

A popular camp and group song. The song is repeated again and again, each time more softly.
Finally the words are only repeated silently to oneself,
until the last line is shouted at the top of the lungs:
John Jacob Jingleheimer Schmidt! Ta-ra-ra-ra-ra-ra-ra-ra!

John   Ja - cob Jin - gle- heim- er Schmidt, His name — is   my   name too; _____

When - ev - er   we   go   out,   Hear the hap - py peo - ple   shout:

John   Ja - cob Jin - gle - heim- er Schmidt! Ta - ra - ra - ra - ra - ra - ra - ra!

A CAPITAL SHIP

In the company of the "Flying Dutchman," the "Golden Vanity" and the other
great ships of story and legend there will always be a small corner
reserved for the "Walloping Window Blind."
The verses are by the American master of nonsense, Charles Edward Carryl.

1. A cap-i-tal ship for an o - cean trip Was the "Wal-lop-ing Win - dow Blind."
2. The boat- swain's mate was __ very se - date Yet __ fond __ of a - muse - ment, too,

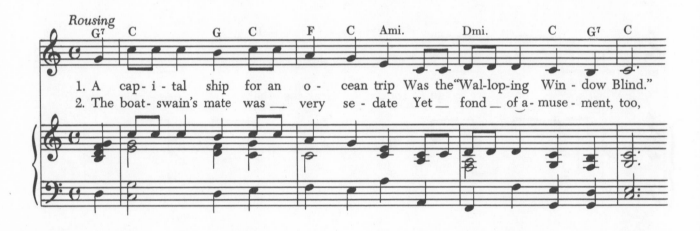

No gale that blew dis-mayed __ her crew, Or trou-bled the cap - tain's mind.
And he played hop-scotch with the star - board watch While the cap - tain tickled the crew.

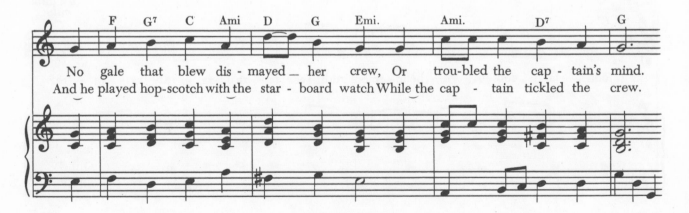

The man at the wheel was _ taught to feel Con - tempt for the wild- est blow- ow- ow,
And the gun-ner we had was ap -parent-ly mad For he sat on the af - ter - rai - ai -ail,

And it of -ten ap-peared, when the weath-er had cleared,That he'd been in his bunk be - low.
And _ fired _ sa - lutes with the cap - tain's boots In the teeth of the boom - ing gale.

3. The captain sat in a Commodore's hat
   And dined in a royal way,
   On toasted pigs and pickles and figs
   And gummery bread each day,
   The cook was Dutch and behaved as such,
   For the food that he gave the crew-ew-ew,
   Was a number of tons of hot-cross buns,
   Chopped up with sugar and glue.   (Chorus)

4. And we all felt ill as mariners will
   On a diet that's cheap and rude,
   And we shivered and shook as we dipped the cook
   In a tub of his gluesome food.
   Then nautical pride we laid aside,
   And we cast the vessel asho-o-ore
   On the Gulliby Isles where the Pooh-pooh smiles
   And the Anagazanders roar.   (Chorus)

5. Composed of sand was that favored land,
   And trimmed with cinnamon straws;
   And pink and blue was the pleasing hue
   Of the Tickletoeteaser's claws.
   And we sat on the edge of a sandy ledge
   And shot at the whistling bee-ee-ee,
   And the Binnacle-bats wore waterproof hats,
   As they danced in the sounding sea.   (Chorus)

6. On rubagub bark, from dawn to dark,
   We fed, till we all had grown
   Uncommonly shrunk—when a Chinese junk
   Came by from the torriby zone.
   She was stubby and square, but we didn't much care
   And we cheerily put to sea-ee-ee,
   And we left the crew of the junk to chew
   The bark of the rubagub tree.   (Chorus)

CHORUS:

   So, blow, ye winds, hi-ho,
   A-sailing we will go,
   We'll stay no more on England's shore
   So let the music play-ay-ay.
   I'm off for the morning train,
   I'll cross the raging main,
   I'm off to my love with a boxing glove
   Ten thousand miles away.

I CAN'T DO THAT SUM

From Victor Herbert's well-known operetta "Babes in Toyland."
The words are by Glen MacDonough.

With charm

1. If a steam-ship weighed ten thou-sand tons And sailed five thou-sand miles,
2. If a pound of prunes cost thir-teen cents At half past one to-day,

With — car - go large of o - ver - shoes And car - ving knives and files,
And the gro - cer is so bald he wears A dol lar - five tou - pée,

If the mates were al - most six feet high And the bo - s'n near the same,
And — if with ev - 'ry pound of tea He will give two cut - glass plates,

Would you sub - tract or mul - ti - ply To find the cap - tain's name?
How soon be - fore Wil - lie falls down On his new rol - ler skates?

Oh, _____ oh, _____ oh. _____

Put down six and car-ry two, Ah, ah, ah; ah, ah, ah;

Gee! but this is hard to do, Ah, ah, ah; ah, ah, ah.

You can think and think and think Till your brains are numb,

I don't care what teach-er says, I can't do that sum.

THE WORLD TURNED UPSIDE DOWN

*Songs and poems that turn the everyday world upside down appear in the
literature and folklore of almost every country, from ancient times to
our own day. This song goes back to the days of the American Revolution.*

Flowing

If but-ter-cups buzz'd af-ter the bee,

If boats were on land, church-es on sea,

If sum-mer were spring and the o-ther way round,

Then all the world would be up-side down.

FOOBA-WOOBA JOHN

Half the fun of Fooba-Wooba John lies in making up new verses.
Rhymes are not really required. The only rule is to keep it silly.

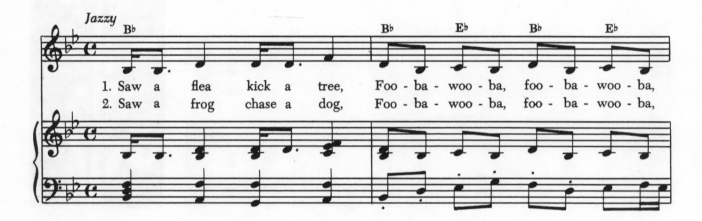

1. Saw a flea kick a tree, Foo-ba-woo-ba, foo-ba-woo-ba,
2. Saw a frog chase a dog, Foo-ba-woo-ba, foo-ba-woo-ba,

Saw a flea kick a tree, Foo-ba-woo-ba John;
Saw a frog chase a dog, Foo-ba-woo-ba John;

Saw a flea kick a tree In the mid-dle of the sea.
Saw a frog chase a dog Sit-ting on a hol-low log.

Hey, John, ho, John, Foo-ba-woo-ba John.
Hey, John, ho, John, Foo-ba-woo-ba John.

3. Saw a snail chase a whale,
Fooba-wooba, fooba-wooba,
Saw a snail chase a whale,
Fooba-wooba John;
Saw a snail chase a whale
All around the water pail.
Hey, John, ho, John,
Fooba-wooba John.

4. Heard a cow say me-ow,
Fooba-wooba, fooba-wooba,
Heard a cow say me-ow,
Fooba-wooba John;
Heard a cow say me-ow,
Then I heard it say bow-wow.
Hey, John, ho, John,
Fooba-wooba John.

MICHAEL FINNEGAN

*The last "Begin again!" is an invitation to start the whole song over,
an invitation children rarely can be prevailed upon to refuse.*

Energetic

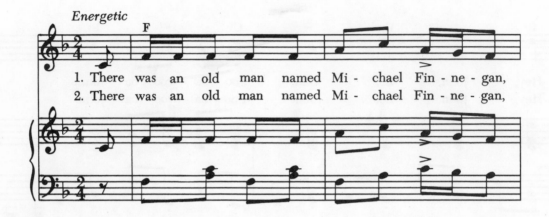

1. There was an old man named Mi - chael Fin - ne - gan,
2. There was an old man named Mi - chael Fin - ne - gan,

He had whisk - ers on his chin - ne - gan,
He kicked up an aw - ful din - ne - gan,

A - long came the wind and blew them in a - gain,
Be - cause they___ said he must not sing a - gain,

138

Poor old Mi - chael Fin - ne - gan. Be - gin a - gain.
Poor old Mi - chael Fin - ne - gan. Be - gin a - gain.

3. There was an old man named Michael Finnegan,
   He went fishing with a pinnegan,
   Caught a fish and dropped it in again,
   Poor old Michael Finnegan.
   Begin again.

4. There was an old man named Michael Finnegan,
   He grew fat and then grew thin again,
   Then he died and had to begin again,
   Poor old Michael Finnegan.
   Begin again.

IF ALL THE RAINDROPS

A sweet fantasy for gloomy days.

If all ____ the rain- drops were lem- on drops and gum- drops,

Oh, what a rain it would be!

I'd stand out- side with my mouth o- pen wide,

That's ____ the weath- er for me, oh ba- by!

140

I would-n't care if the sun would nev - er shine,

I'd keep on wish - ing for rain - drops all the time. If

all ___ the rain - drops were lem - on drops and gum - drops,

Oh, what a rain it would be!

141

MY UNCLE ROASTED A KANGAROO

The tune is from Gounod's Faust. The words, needless to say, are not.

My un - cle roast - ed a kang - a - roo,

Gave me the griz - zel - ly end to chew.

Was that a ver - y nice thing to do,

To give me the griz - zly end of a kang - a - roo _____ to chew?

142

BOOM, BOOM, AIN'T IT GREAT TO BE CRAZY?

There is something of the unique joy and exuberance and madness of childhood in this well-known song.

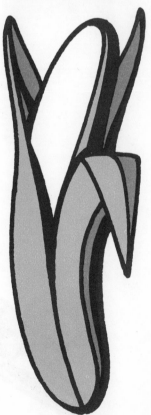

Bouncing and rhythmic

F   C   F   C

1. A horse and a flea and the three blind mice
2. Way down South where ba-na-nas grow,

F   C   F   C

Sat on a curb-stone shoot-ing dice,
A flea stepped on an e-le-phant's toe,

F   C⁷   F   C⁷

The horse he slipped and fell on the flea,
The e-le-phant cried with tears in his eyes,

143

"Whoops," said the flea, "there's a horse __ on me!"
"Why don't you pick on __ some-one your size?"

Chorus

Boom, boom, ain't it great to be cra - zy?

Boom, boom, ain't it great to be cra - zy?

Gid - dy and fool - ish the whole day through,

Boom, boom, ain't it great to be cra - zy?

3. Way up North where there's ice and snow
   There lived a penguin and his name was Joe,
   He got so tired of black and white,
   He wore pink slacks to the dance last night. (*Chorus*)

CHORUS:

Boom, boom, ain't it great to be crazy?
Boom, boom, ain't it great to be crazy?
Giddy and foolish the whole day through,
Boom, boom, ain't it great to be crazy?

I WAS BORN ABOUT TEN THOUSAND YEARS AGO

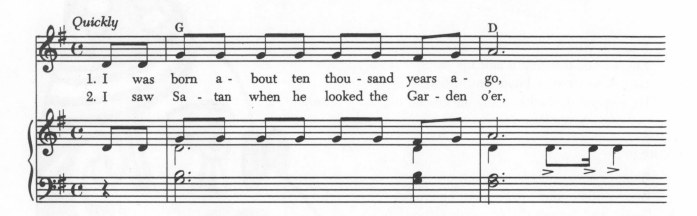

Quickly

1. I was born a - bout ten thou - sand years a - go,
2. I saw Sa - tan when he looked the Gar - den o'er,

And there's no - thing in the world that I don't know,
Saw ___ Eve and A - dam driv - en from the door,

I saw Pe - ter, Paul and Mo - ses play - ing ring a - round the ro - ses,
And be - hind the bush - es peep - ing saw the ap - ple they were eat - ing,

And I'll lick the guy who says it is - n't so.
And I'll swear that I'm the guy that ate the core.

3. I taught Solomon to learn his ABC's,
   I helped Brigham Young to make Limburger cheese,
   And while sailing down the bay with Methuselah one day,
   I saved his flowing whiskers from the breeze.

4. I taught Samson how to use his mighty hand,
   I showed Columbus this here happy land,
   And for Pharaoh's little kiddies built all the Pyramiddies
   And to Sahara carried all the sand.

MULES

When all the befores and behinds of "Mules" are untangled the song actually makes a little sense. The tune is the same as "Auld Lang Syne."

On mules we find two legs be-hind And two we find be-fore,

We stand be-hind be-fore we find What the two be-hind be for.

When we're be-hind the two be-hind, We find what these be for,

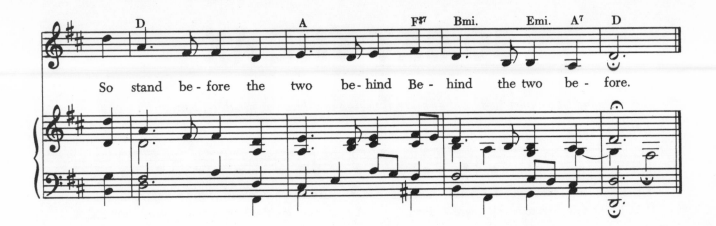

So stand be-fore the two be-hind Be-hind the two be-fore.

GO GET THE AX

A song so completely devoid of sense it begins to take on a peculiar logic of its own.

1. Peep - ing through the knot - hole ___ Of Grand - pa's wood - en leg; ___
2. I fell from a win - dow, ___ A se - cond - stor - y win - dow, ___

Who'll wind the clock when I am gone? ___
Why do they build the shore so near the o - cean? ___

Go get the ax, ___ there's a flea in Liz - zie's ear,
Who cut the sleeves ___ out of dear old Dad - dy's vest,

And a boy's best ___ friend ___ is his moth - er. ___
And dug up Fi - do's bones to build a sew - er? ___

BILL GROGAN'S GOAT

*The identity of Bill Grogan has faded into obscurity, but the fame and glory
of his omnivorous and ingenious goat lives on.*

1. Bill Gro - gan's goat   Was feel - ing fine,
2. Bill grabbed that goat   By the wool of his back,

Ate three red shirts   Right off the line.
And tied him to   The rail - road track.

3. That goat he bucked
   With might and main,
   As round the curve
   Came a passenger train.

4. That goat he bucked
   With might and main,
   Coughed up those shirts
   And flagged the train.

151

The Animal Fair

*An old minstrel-show song. The words "The monk" at the end are usually
repeated again and again like a broken record. And sometimes hours,
or even days after the song has been sung, some child will suddenly pipe up with one last "The monk!"*

I went to the a - ni - mal fair, ____ The birds and the beasts were there, ____

The big ba - boon by the light of the moon Was comb - ing his au - burn hair. ____

The mon - key he got drunk, ____ And fell on the e - le - phant's trunk; ____

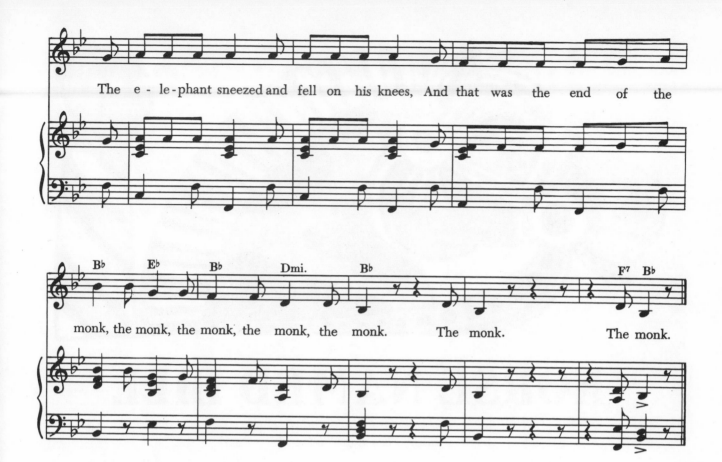

The e-le-phant sneezed and fell on his knees, And that was the end of the

monk, the monk, the monk, the monk, the monk. The monk. The monk.

HORSE NAMED BILL

A "darn fool ditty," to use Carl Sandburg's epithet, if there ever was one. The tune is based on "Dixie."

Bouncy / B♭

1. Oh, I had a horse and his name was Bill,
2. He ran so ___ fast he ___ could not stop,

E♭

And when he ran he could-n't stand still;
He ran in-to a bar-ber shop,

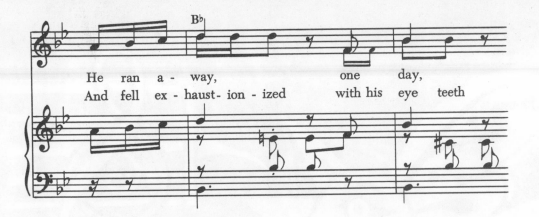

He ran a - way, one day,
And fell ex - haust - ion - ized with his eye teeth

And al - so I ran with him.
In the bar - ber's _____ left shoul - der.

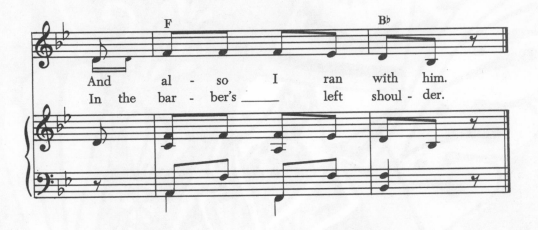

3. Oh, I went up in a balloon so big,
   The people on the earth they looked like a pig,
   Like a mice, like a katydid,
   Like flieses — and like fleasens.

4. The balloon turned up with its bottom side higher,
   It fell on the wife of a country squire.
   She made a noise like a dog hound,
   Like a steam whistle — and like dynamite.

5. Oh, what could you do in a case like that?
   What could you do but stamp on your hat,
   Or your toothbrush, or your grandmother,
   Or anything that's helpless?

155

The singing games that follow fall into two general categories: "Do-as-I-do" or imitative games, and circle games.

The "Do-as-I-do" games are all of the follow-the-leader type and need no explanation other than that which the songs themselves provide. They are the simplest singing games of all and are beloved by children of pre-school and kindergarten age (fours, fives and young sixes). They can be sung and played by large groups of children in schools, play groups or at parties. They can also be played by one child and a parent at home.

The circle games selected here are all easy to learn and fun to sing and play. Although enjoyed by older boys and girls, they are most often played by children in the early primary grades (ages six, seven, eight and nine). Children often enjoy improvising new words and actions for these games.

A few words about learning and singing rounds will be found on page 185.

COME ON AND JOIN IN TO THE GAME

There are many ways to play this game. A parent or teacher may sing all the words and the children can perform the actions at the proper places. Or a different child can be leader for each verse, deciding which action to do while the others imitate him, until each child has had his turn as leader.

To quicken the pace, the leader may change the action twice in each verse, with a different child singing the second line and performing a different action, instead of repeating the first line. Both actions are then performed in order after the last line.

Other actions suitable for this game: whistling, shaking hands, nodding heads, crying, snoring.

1. Let ev - 'ry - one clap hands like me. *(clap, clap)*
2. Let ev - 'ry - one sneeze __ like me. *(ker- choo!)*

Let ev - 'ry - one clap hands like me. *(clap, clap)*
Let ev - 'ry - one sneeze __ like me. *(ker - choo!)*

Come on and join in to the game,
Come on and join in to the game,

You'll find that it's al - ways the same. *(clap, clap)*
You'll find that it's al - ways the same. *(ker - choo!)*

3. Let everyone yawn like me. *(yawn)*
   Let everyone yawn like me. *(yawn)*
   Come on and join in to the game,
   You'll find that it's always the same. *(yawn)*

4. Let everyone jump up like me. *(jump)*
   Let everyone jump up like me. *(jump)*
   Come on and join in to the game,
   You'll find that it's always the same. *(jump)*

5. Let everyone sit down like me. *(sit)*
   Let everyone sit down like me. *(sit)*
   Come on and join in to the game,
   You'll find that it's always the same. *(sit)*

6. Let everyone laugh like me. *(ha-ha)*
   Let everyone laugh like me. *(ha-ha)*
   Come on and join in to the game,
   You'll find that it's always the same. *(ha-ha)*

CLAP YOUR HANDS

A simple singing game in which children perform the actions in time to the music (as indicated by crosses [x]), and continue the actions during the musical interlude. Children may sit, stand in a circle or march around the room while singing.

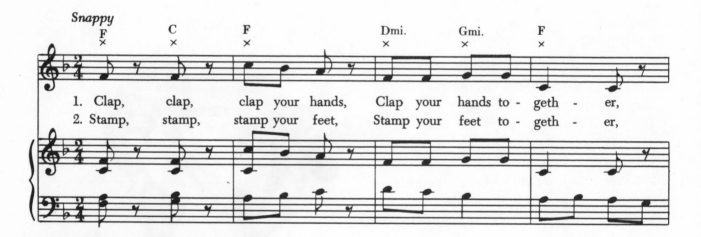

Snappy

1. Clap, clap, clap your hands, Clap your hands to-geth-er,
2. Stamp, stamp, stamp your feet, Stamp your feet to-geth-er,

Clap, clap, clap your hands, Clap your hands to-geth-er.
Stamp, stamp, stamp your feet, Stamp your feet to-geth-er.

(Clap)

3. Nod, nod, nod your head,
   Nod your heads together,
   Nod, nod, nod your head,
   Nod your heads together.

4. Shake, shake, shake your head,
   Shake your heads together,
   Shake, shake, shake your head,
   Shake your heads together.

5. Stretch, stretch, stretch up high,
   Stretch up high together,
   Stretch, stretch, stretch up high,
   Stretch up high together.

6. Dig, dig, dig the ground,
   Dig the ground together,
   Dig, dig, dig the ground,
   Dig the ground together.

7. Crawl, crawl, crawl along,
   Crawl along together,
   Crawl, crawl, crawl along,
   Crawl along together.

DID YOU EVER SEE A LASSIE?

FORMATION: *Standing in a circle, the children hold hands. One child, chosen to be the Lassie (or Laddie), stands in the middle.*

ACTION: *Everyone circles to the left and sings the song. At the words* this way and that *in measures 7 and 8, the child in the center performs some action of her choosing. The others stop circling at the end of measure 8, drop hands and imitate the Las-*

sie's action. When they have sung the song through, the Lassie or Laddie chooses another child to be the next leader and steps back into the circle. The song is then sung again.

Suitable actions for this game: nodding head to left and right, hopping on left foot and then on right foot, snapping fingers to the left and right, clapping in front and behind.

162

Go this way and that way, and this way and that way,

Did you ev - er see a las - sie go this way and that?

PUT YOUR FINGER IN THE AIR

A beloved Do-As-I-Do game. Older children like to make up new verses, such as "Put your finger on your shoulder...And leave it till you're older."

Moderately fast

1. Put your fin-ger in the air, in the air,
2. Put your fin-ger on your head, on your head,

Put your fin-ger in the air, in the air,
Put your fin-ger on your head, on your head,

Put your fin - ger in the air, Tell me, how's the air up there?
Put your fin - ger on your head, Tell me, is it green or red?

Put your fin - ger in the air,___ in the air.
Put your fin - ger on your head,___ on your head.

3. Put your finger on your cheek, on your cheek,
   Put your finger on your cheek, on your cheek,
   Put your finger on your cheek,
   Leave it there about a week,
   Put your finger on your cheek, on your cheek.

4. Put your finger on your nose, on your nose,
   Put your finger on your nose, on your nose,
   Put your finger on your nose,
   Is that where the cold wind blows?
   Put your finger on your nose.

5. Put your finger on your chest, on your chest,
   Put your finger on your chest, on your chest,
   Put your finger on your chest,
   Give it just a little rest,
   Put your finger on your chest, on your chest.

6. Put your finger on your belly, on your belly,
   Put your finger on your belly, on your belly,
   Put your finger on your belly,
   Make it shake like apple jelly,
   Put your finger on your belly, on your belly.

HA-HA, THIS-A-WAY

One child stands in the center of the circle for this game and walks or skips or marches in the manner of the person mentioned in the verse. For the chorus, all children go around in the circle imitating the leader. A different child becomes leader for each verse until all children have had a chance. Other occupations—carpenter, barber, etc. —are better adapted to pantomime without marching or skipping.

Smoothly

1. When I was a young girl, young girl, young girl,
2. When I was a sol - dier, sol - dier, sol - dier,

When I was a young girl, then, oh, then.
When I was a sol - dier, then, oh, then.

Chorus:

Ha - ha, this - a - way, ha - ha, that - a - way,

Ha - Ha, this - a - way, then, oh, then.

3. When I was a cowboy, cowboy, cowboy,
When I was a cowboy, then, oh, then. *(Chorus)*

4. When I was an Indian, Indian, Indian,
When I was an Indian, then, oh, then. *(Chorus)*

5. When I was an old man, old man, old man,
When I was on old man, then, oh, then. *(Chorus)*

CHORUS:
Ha-ha, this-a-way, ha-ha, that-a-way,
Ha-ha, this-a-way, then, oh, then.

167

THE HOKEY-POKEY

The game is played as the words indicate, with the children in a line or forming a circle. The hokey-pokey motion is a hula-type wriggle. The words "And that's what it's all about" are simply sung, with no action, and are followed by a loud clap at "Hey!"

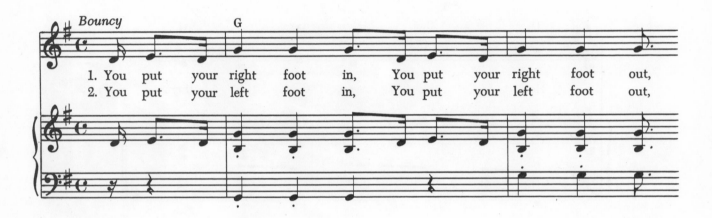

1. You put your right foot in, You put your right foot out,
2. You put your left foot in, You put your left foot out,

You put your right foot in And you shake it all a-bout,
You put your left foot in And you shake it all a-bout,

And then you do the ho-key-po-key, And you turn your-self a-bout,
And then you do the ho-key-po-key And you turn your-self a-bout,

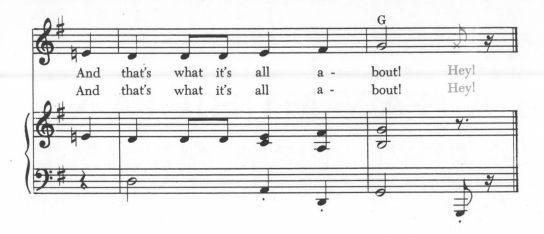

And that's what it's all a - bout! Hey!
And that's what it's all a - bout! Hey!

3. You put your right hand in, *etc.*

4. You put your left hand in, *etc.*

5. You put your right shoulder in, *etc.*

6. You put your left shoulder in, *etc.*

7. You put your right hip in, *etc.*

8. You put your left hip in, *etc.*

9. You put your whole self in, *etc.*

I AM A GAY MUSICIAN

The children stand in a circle and sing the song, pantomiming the playing of each instrument. At the words "Skipping and playing, Singing and swaying," the children skip about to the left, or sway to the right and to the left.

1. I am a gay mu-si-cian, from Lon-don I have come,
2. I am a gay mu-si-cian, I come from old Ber-lin,

And I can play sweet mu-sic up-on my lit-tle drum.
And I can play sweet mu-sic up-on my vi-o-lin.

Trr - um- pum- pum, Trr - um-pum- pum, Trr - um- pum- pum, trr - um-pum- pum,
Fid-dle dee- dee- dee, fid-dle dee- dee- dee, Fid-dle dee- dee- dee, fid-dle dee-dee- dee,

Skip - ping and play - ing, Sing - ing and sway - ing,
Skip - ping and play - ing, Sing - ing and sway - ing,

Trr - um - pum - pum, trr - um - pum - pum, trr - um - pum - pum - pum - pum.
Fid - dle - dee - dee - dee, fid - dle - dee - dee - dee, fid - dle - dee - dee - dee - dee - dee.

3. I am a gay musician, in Paris I was born,
   And I can play sweet music upon my big French horn,
   Baw-baw-baw-baw-baw, baw-baw-baw-baw-baw,
   Baw-baw-baw-baw-baw, baw-baw-baw-baw-baw,
   Skipping and playing,
   Singing and swaying,
   Baw-baw-baw-baw-baw, baw-baw-baw-baw-baw,
   Baw-baw-baw-baw-baw-baw-baw!

4. I am a gay musician, the best you've ever met,
   And I can play sweet music upon my clarinet,
   Doodle-doo-doo-doo, doodle-doo-doo-doo, *etc.*

5. I am a gay musician, I've traveled very far,
   And I can play sweet music upon my fine guitar,
   Plunky-plunk-plunk-plunk, plunky-plunk-plunk-plunk, *etc.*

6. I am a gay musician, just listen to me toot,
   And I can play sweet music upon my silver flute,
   (Whistle the tune)
   Skipping and playing,
   Singing and swaying,
   (Whistle the tune).

171

THE MULBERRY BUSH

FORMATION: *Children hold hands and stand in a circle.*

ACTION: Verse 1: *Children circle to the left and drop hands at the end of the verse.*

Verses 2-8: *Children act out the words of each verse in time to the music.*

At the end, Verse 1 is sung again as the children circle to the right, holding hands.

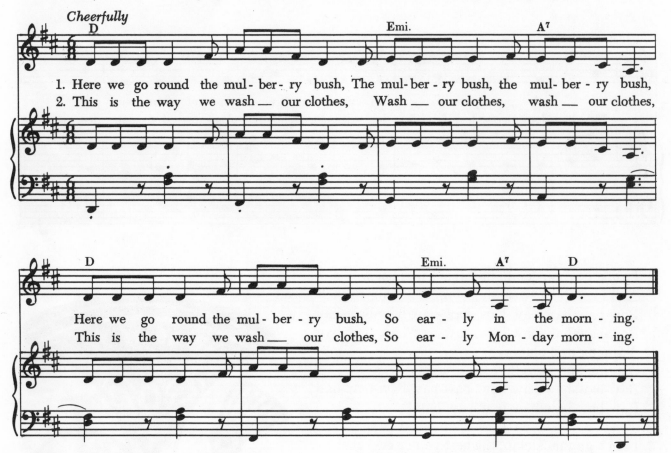

1. Here we go round the mul-ber-ry bush, The mul-ber-ry bush, the mul-ber-ry bush,
2. This is the way we wash our clothes, Wash our clothes, wash our clothes,

Here we go round the mul-ber-ry bush, So ear-ly in the morn-ing.
This is the way we wash our clothes, So ear-ly Mon-day morn-ing.

3. This is the way we iron our clothes,
   Iron our clothes, iron our clothes,
   This is the way we iron our clothes,
   So early Tuesday morning.

4. This is the way we scrub the floor,
   Scrub the floor, scrub the floor,
   This is the way we scrub the floor,
   So early Wednesday morning.

5. This is the way we sweep the house,
   Sweep the house, sweep the house,
   This is the way we sweep the house,
   So early Thursday morning.

6. This is the way we make a cake,
   Make a cake, make a cake,
   This is the way we make a cake,
   So early Friday morning.

7. This is the way we brush our hair,
   Brush our hair, brush our hair,
   This is the way we brush our hair,
   So early Saturday morning.

8. This is the way we go to church,
   Go to church, go to church,
   This is the way we go to church,
   So early Sunday morning.

FORMATION: *Children sit in a circle on the floor, remove their shoes and hold them in their hands.*

ACTION: *The players hold shoes in front of them, one in each hand. The song is sung slowly at first, in a regular tempo. The children pass the shoes to the left on the down beats of measures 1, 3, and 5 (as indicated by asterisks in the music), setting them down in front of the next child with a thump. In measure 7 each player thumps the shoes in front of the player on the left at the word* this, *without letting go of the shoes, and then thumps them in front of the player at the right on the word* what, *finally placing them again in front of the player on the left at the word* do *in measure 8, this time leaving them there. The song continues and when the rhythm is well established the tempo is gradually speeded up, until it is sung as fast as possible.*

PASS THE SHOE

173

BLUEBIRD

FORMATION: *Standing in a circle, the children hold hands up to form arches. One child, chosen to be the Bluebird, stands outside the circle.*

ACTION:

Verse 1: *The Bluebird weaves in and out through the arches with a skipping step.*

Verse 2: *The Bluebird stops behind one child and taps him or her on the shoulder in time to the music. At the end of the verse the first Bluebird places his hands on the shoulders of this second Bluebird.*

The song is now repeated with the two Bluebirds weaving in and out through the arches, the second Bluebird leading. At the repetition of Verse 2 a third Bluebird is chosen and the three children weave through. The game continues until there are only two children remaining to form an arch and these become the first two Bluebirds of the next game.

Last repetition: *The children sing the first verse, gradually decreasing the tempo, yawning and pantomiming fatigue. At the final line—"Oh Johnny, I am tired"—all children collapse in a heap on the floor and pretend to fall asleep.*

1. Blue - bird, blue - bird, on ___ my ___ win - dow,
2. Take a lit - tle boy, tap him on the shoul - der,
          girl,   her

Blue - bird, blue - bird, on ___ my ___ win - dow,
Take a lit - tle boy, tap him on the shoul - der,
     girl,   her

Blue - bird, blue - bird, on ___ my ___ win - dow,
Take a lit - tle boy, tap him on the shoul - der,
girl, her

Oh John - ny, I am tir ___ ed.
Oh John - ny, I am tir ___ ed.

A-TISKET, A-TASKET

FORMATION: *A circle. One child chosen to be "It" stands outside the circle holding a handkerchief.*

ACTION: *Children sing the song and the one who is "It" skips around the outside of the circle. Somewhere between measures 8*

and 12, "It" drops the handkerchief behind any child he chooses. He then races around the circle in the same direction he has been going, while the child behind whom it has been dropped runs in the opposite direction. The last one to get back to the handkerchief is now "It" and the game begins again.

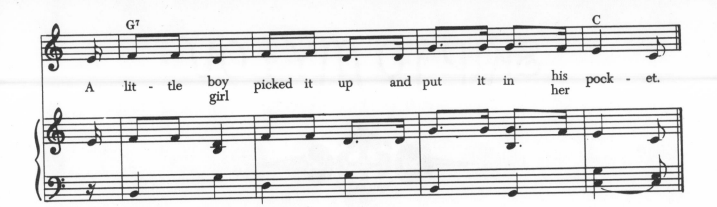

A lit - tle boy picked it up and put it in his pock - et.
girl   her

SKIP TO MY LOU

FORMATION: *A single circle with one child in the middle.*

ACTION:

Chorus: *As the singing starts, the child in the middle chooses a partner and the two skip around inside the circle while the others sing and clap. At measure 7 of the chorus the first child joins the circle, leaving the second child in the middle.*

Verse 1: *The child now in the middle skips around the inside of the circle alone,* while the others sing the verse. At measure 15 he picks a partner.

Repeat Chorus: *Both children skip around inside the circle. The first child goes back to the circle at the last line of chorus.*

Verses 2-6: *The action of Verse 1 is repeated for each verse, always followed by chorus. The children forming the circle may pantomime the activities of each verse, and can easily improvise new verses to prolong the game.*

1. Lost my __ part - ner, what-'ll I __ do? Lost my __ part - ner, what-'ll I __ do?
2. I'll get an - oth - er one, pret - ti - er than you, I'll get an - oth - er one, pret - ti - er than you,

MEASURE 15

Lost my __ part - ner, what-'ll I __ do? Skip to my Lou, my dar - ling.
I'll get an - oth - er one, pret - ti - er than you, Skip to my Lou, my dar - ling.

3. Flies in the buttermilk, shoo, fly, shoo, *(3 times)*
   Skip to my Lou, my darling. *(Chorus)*

4. Cows in the barnyard, moo, moo, moo, *(3 times)*
   Skip to my Lou, my darling. *(Chorus)*

5. Train is a-coming, choo, choo, choo, *(3 times)*
   Skip to my Lou, my darling. *(Chorus)*

CHORUS:
Lou, Lou, skip to my Lou,
Lou, Lou, skip to my Lou,
Lou, Lou, skip to my Lou,
Skip to my Lou, my darling.

THE FARMER IN THE DELL

FORMATION: *A circle with one child chosen to be the Farmer standing in the middle.*

ACTION:

Verse 1: *Children, singing, circle around the Farmer.*

Verse 2: *The Farmer chooses one child from the circle to be the Wife, and the Wife moves into the center of the circle with him. Other children circle around them and sing.*

Verses 3-8: *A new child is chosen for a* role *in each verse and joins the Farmer and the others in the center of the circle while the remaining children circle around them and sing.*

Verses 9-15: *One child runs away in each verse and rejoins the circle until only the child chosen to be the Cheese is left in the middle of the circle.*

Verse 16: *All the children jump up and down and clap hands loudly at the Cheese, who becomes the Farmer in the next game.*

1. The farm - er in the dell, _____ The farm - er in the dell,
2. The farm - er takes a wife, _____ The farm - er takes a wife,

Hi - ho, the der - ri - o, The farm - er in the dell.
Hi - ho, the der - ri - o, The farm - er takes a wife.

3. The wife takes a child,
   The wife takes a child,
   Hi-ho, the derrio,
   The wife takes a child.

4. The child takes a nurse, *etc.*

5. The nurse takes a dog, *etc.*

6. The dog takes a cat, *etc.*

7. The cat takes a rat, *etc.*

8. The rat takes the cheese, *etc.*

9. The farmer runs away, *etc.*

10. The wife runs away, *etc.*

11. The child runs away, *etc.*

12. The nurse runs away, *etc.*

13. The dog runs away, *etc.*

14. The cat runs away, *etc.*

15. The rat runs away, *etc.*

16. The cheese stands alone,
    The cheese stands alone,
    Hi-ho, the derrio,
    The cheese stands alone.

180

Oats, Peas, Beans and Barley Grow

FORMATION: *Children hold hands, standing in a circle. One child, chosen to be the Farmer, stands in the center of the circle.*

ACTION: *Chorus—Children circle to the right and around the Farmer, singing.*

Verse 1: The Farmer performs the actions—first sowing the seed, then standing at ease, stamping, clapping and turning around while shading his eyes with his hands. At the end of the verse the Farmer points his finger at another child who be- *comes the new Farmer in the next verse.*

Repeat Chorus: Children circle around new Farmer, singing.

Verses 2-4: Same as Verse 1, with new Farmer performing the actions described in each verse—watering, hoeing and gathering—and choosing a new Farmer at the end of each verse. Chorus is repeated after each verse.

The game is repeated until each child has had a chance to be Farmer.

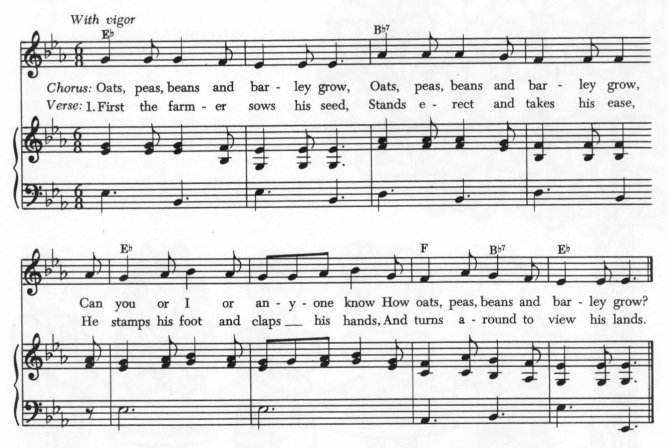

With vigor

Chorus: Oats, peas, beans and bar - ley grow, Oats, peas, beans and bar - ley grow,
Verse: 1. First the farm - er sows his seed, Stands e - rect and takes his ease,

Can you or I or an - y - one know How oats, peas, beans and bar - ley grow?
He stamps his foot and claps ___ his hands, And turns a - round to view his lands.

2. Next the farmer waters the seed,
   Stands erect and takes his ease,
   He stamps his foot and claps his hands
   And turns around to view his lands. *(Chorus)*

3. Next the farmer hoes the weeds,
   Stands erect and takes his ease,
   He stamps his foot and claps his hands
   And turns around to view his lands. *(Chorus)*

4. Last the farmer harvests his seed,
   Stands erect and takes his ease,
   He stamps his foot and claps his hands
   And turns around to view his lands. *(Chorus)*

CHORUS:
Oats, peas, beans and barley grow,
Oats, peas, beans and barley grow,
Can you or I or anyone know
How oats, peas, beans and barley grow?

THE ALLEE ALLEE-O

FORMATION: *Children stand next to each other in a line, holding hands. The first child at the left end of the line holds on to a post or leans hand against a tree or a wall, forming a bridge.*

ACTION: *As the children sing the song, the Leader (the child at the right end of the line) leads the others under the bridge, thus turning the first child around. He returns to the end and then leads the line between the first child and the second, thus turning the second child around. As each child is turned around he ends up facing the opposite direction from the rest of the line. The players continue singing until every child is turned around. Then the singing is resumed as the children unwind.*

To unwind: the child next to the Leader lifts his left arm and pulls the Leader back through. Then the next child pulls both these players through. Then the next pulls these three through, and so on until all the players are unwound.

The Leader and the first child then join hands and the song is sung a last time while all the children skip around in a circle.

182

O the big ship's a-sailing on the Al - lee Al - lee-o,

The Al - lee Al - lee-o, the Al - lee Al - lee-o,

O the big ship's a-sailing on the Al - lee Al - lee-o,

Hi, ding - dong day.

THE NOBLE DUKE OF YORK

FORMATION: *A circle, hands joined. One child chosen to be Fox stands outside the circle.*

ACTION:

Verse 1: *Children circle to the left while singing the first two lines, and the Fox skips to the right outside the circle. Children circle to the right while singing the other two lines, and the Fox skips to the left outside the circle.*

Verse 2: *The two children nearest the Fox raise their arms and force the Fox into the circle by bringing the arch down on the other side of him. Children sing and slowly close ranks, holding hands and walking toward center of circle. They trap the Fox within a tight circle and bounce him around until the word go, when they raise their arms and let him free. He chooses another child to be the next Fox and the game is repeated.*

1. Oh, the no-ble Duke of York,___ He had ten thou-sand men,___
2. Oh, a-hunt-ing we will go,___ A-hunt-ing we will go,___

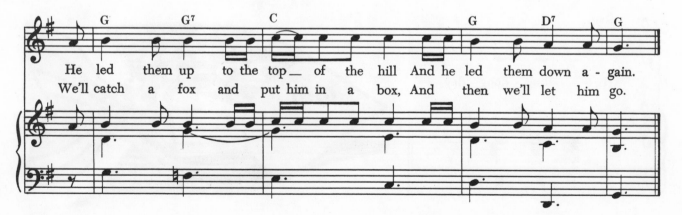

He led them up to the top_ of the hill And he led them down a-gain.
We'll catch a fox and put him in a box, And then we'll let him go.

ROUNDS

A word about rounds: The best way to learn a new round is to sing it from beginning to end several times first, until the words and tune are almost memorized, before attempting it in parts.

The singers are divided into as many groups as there are parts to the round. Group One begins. When Group One reaches Point 2 in the music, Group Two starts singing from the beginning. When Group One reaches Point 3 (and Group Two reaches Point 2), Group Three begins at the beginning, and so on, if there are more than three parts to the round. When each group finishes the last line of the round it immediately begins again at the beginning.

There are two ways to end a round. One is for the groups to stop singing one by one, just as they entered one by one. Thus Group One stops singing when it finishes the last line after a certain number of repetitions. Then each group stops singing when *it* finishes the last line. The last group ends up singing the last line alone.

Another effective way is for everyone to end together. At a prearranged signal, after a certain number of repetitions, everybody stops singing at the next hold (⌒), which is usually at the end of each line, and all groups hold that note to make a nice, full, closing chord.

ROW, ROW, ROW YOUR BOAT

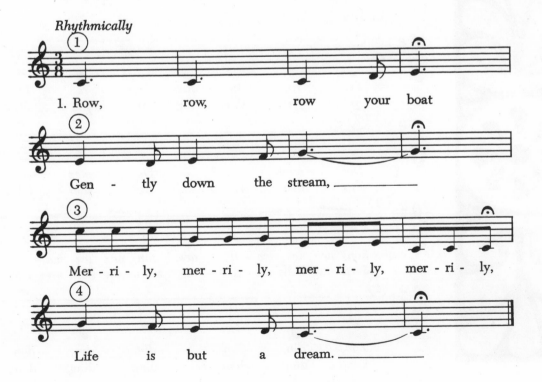

Rhythmically

1. Row,   row,   row   your   boat

Gen - tly   down   the   stream, _____

Mer - ri - ly,   mer - ri - ly,   mer - ri - ly,   mer - ri - ly,

Life   is   but   a   dream. _____

CHAIRS TO MEND

Cheerful

Chairs to mend, old chairs to mend,

Mack - er - el, fresh mack - er - el,

Rags, rags, a - ny old rags?

FRÈRE JACQUES

Lightly

Frè - re Jac - ques, Frè - re Jac - ques,
Are you sleep - ing, are you sleep - ing,

Dor - mez - vous? Dor - mez - vous?
Bro - ther John, Bro - ther John?

Son - nez les ma - ti - nes, son - nez les ma - ti - nes,
Morn - ing bells are ring - ing, morn - ing bells are ring - ing,

Din, din, don; din, din, don.
Ding, ding, dong; ding, ding, dong.

SWEETLY SINGS THE DONKEY

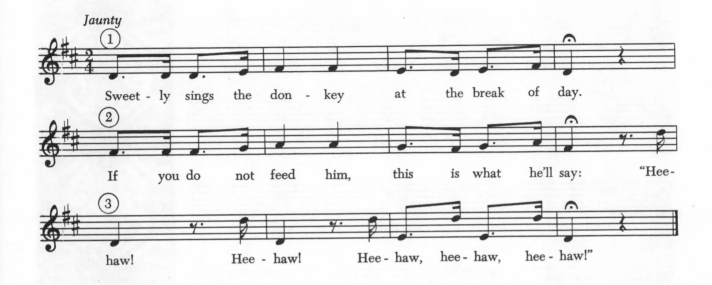

Jaunty

① Sweet - ly sings the don - key at the break of day.

② If you do not feed him, this is what he'll say: "Hee-

③ haw! Hee - haw! Hee - haw, hee - haw, hee - haw!"

THE FROG SONG

Jolly

① Lis - ten to the song of the

② Frogs in yon - der pond:

③ Crick, crick, crick - e - ty crick,

④ Brrr - - - ump!

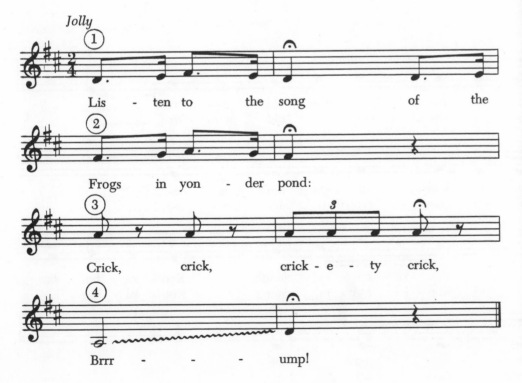

187

SCOTLAND'S BURNING

Quickly

① Scot - land's burn - ing, Scot - land's burn - ing,

② Look out! Look out!

③ Fire! Fire! Fire! Fire!

④ Pour on wa - ter, more wa - ter.

KOOKABURRA

MARION SINCLAIR

Gaily

① 1. Koo - ka - bur - ra sits in the old gum tree, _____
　 2. Koo - ka - bur - ra sits in the old gum tree, _____

② Mer - ry, mer - ry king of the bush is he, _____
　 Eat - ing all the gum - drops he can see, _____

③ Laugh, Koo - ka - bur - ra, laugh, Koo - ka - bur - ra,
　 Stop, Koo - ka - bur - ra, stop, Koo - ka - bur - ra,

④ Gay your life must be.
　 Leave some there for me.

188

WHY SHOULDN'T MY GOOSE

Happily

① Why should-n't my goose

② Sing as well as thy goose,

③ When I paid for my goose

④ Twice as much as thou?

OH, HOW LOVELY IS THE EVENING

Sustained

① Oh, how love-ly is the eve-ning, is the eve-ning,

② When the bells are sweet-ly ring-ing, sweet-ly ring-ing,

③ Ding, dong, ding, dong, ding, dong.

189

HAVE YOU SEEN THE GHOST OF JOHN?

Spookily

① Have you seen the ___ ghost of John?

② Long white bones and the rest all gone, ___

③ Ooh, _____ ooh, ___

④ Would-n't it be chil-ly with no skin on?

190

INDEX

[Song titles appear in capitals, first lines in italics.]